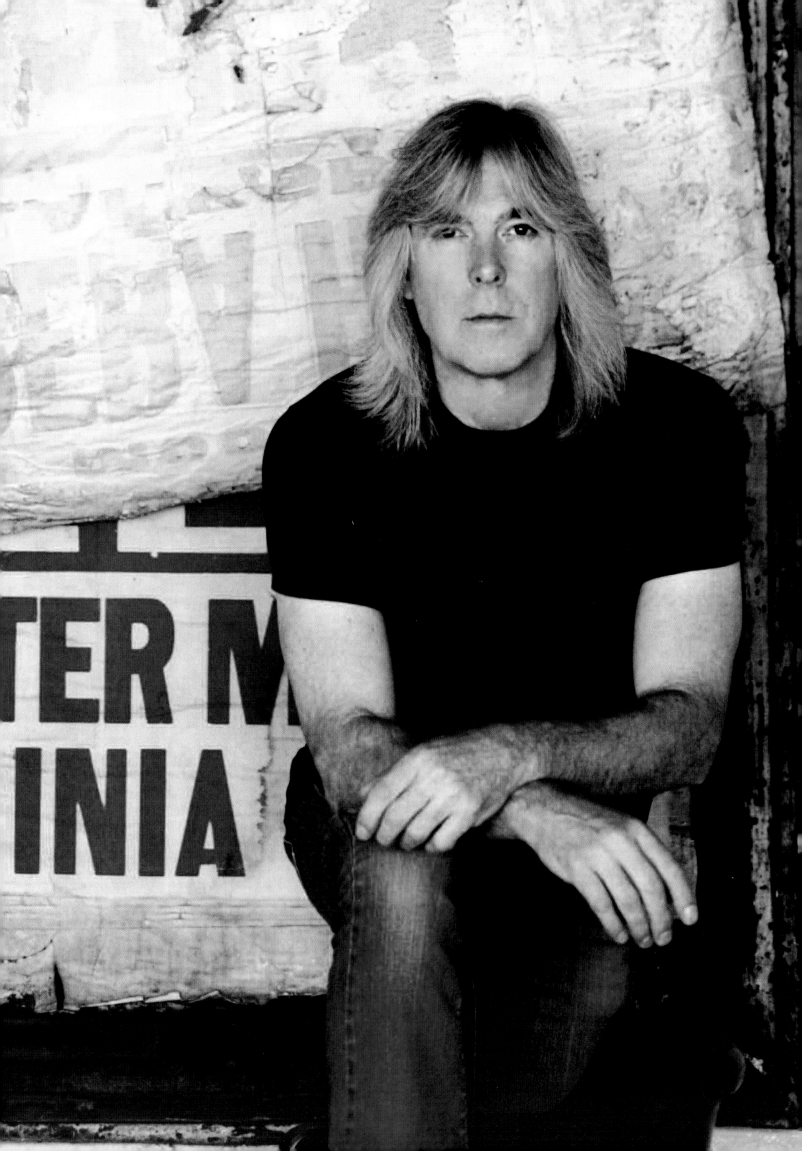

Angus Young: Lead Guitar
Malcolm Young: Rhythm Guitar
Brian Johnson: Vocals
Cliff Williams: Bass Guitar
Phil Rudd: Drums

Photography By Guido Karp

Art Direction & Design By Joshua Marc Levy
Illustrations By Joshua Marc Levy; Containing
Vector Graphics By You Work For Them, LLC

Project editor: David Bradley
Arrangements for publication by Matt Scharfglass,
Martin Shellard, and Hemme B. Luttjeboer

This book Published 2008 by Wise Publications,
a Division of Music Sales Limited.

Order No. AM996666
ISBN: 978-1-84772-954-5

Exclusive Distributors:
Music Sales Limited
14-15 Berners Street, London W1T 3LJ UK
Music Sales Corporation
257 Park Avenue South, New York, NY 10010 USA
Music Sales Pty. Limited
20 Resolution Drive, Caringbah, NSW 2229, Australia

Printed in the EU

Rock N Roll Train

Words & Music by Angus Young & Malcolm Young

14

one cool ___ dev - il.

end Rhythm figure 1

w/Rhythm figure 1 (Guitar 1 on 1st Verse, Guitars 1 and 2 on 2nd Verse)

Your mind on a fan - ta - sy,

liv - in' on the ecs - ta - sy.

Pre-chorus

Give it all, ___ give it, give ___ it what you got.

guitar 1

Rhythm figure 2

guitar 2

Rhythm figure 2a

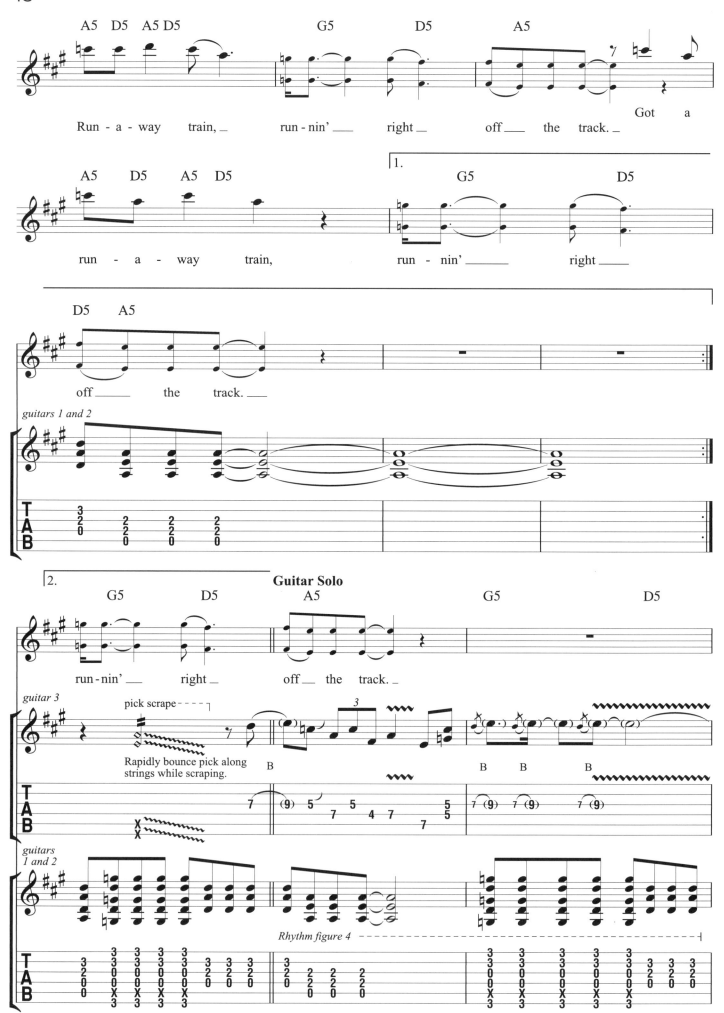

Run - a - way train, ___ run - nin' ___ right ___ off ___ the track. ___ Got a

run - a - way train, run - nin' _____ right _____

off _____ the track. ___

guitars 1 and 2

Guitar Solo

run - nin' ___ right _____ off ___ the track. ___

guitar 3

pick scrape

Rapidly bounce pick along
strings while scraping.

guitars 1 and 2

Rhythm figure 4

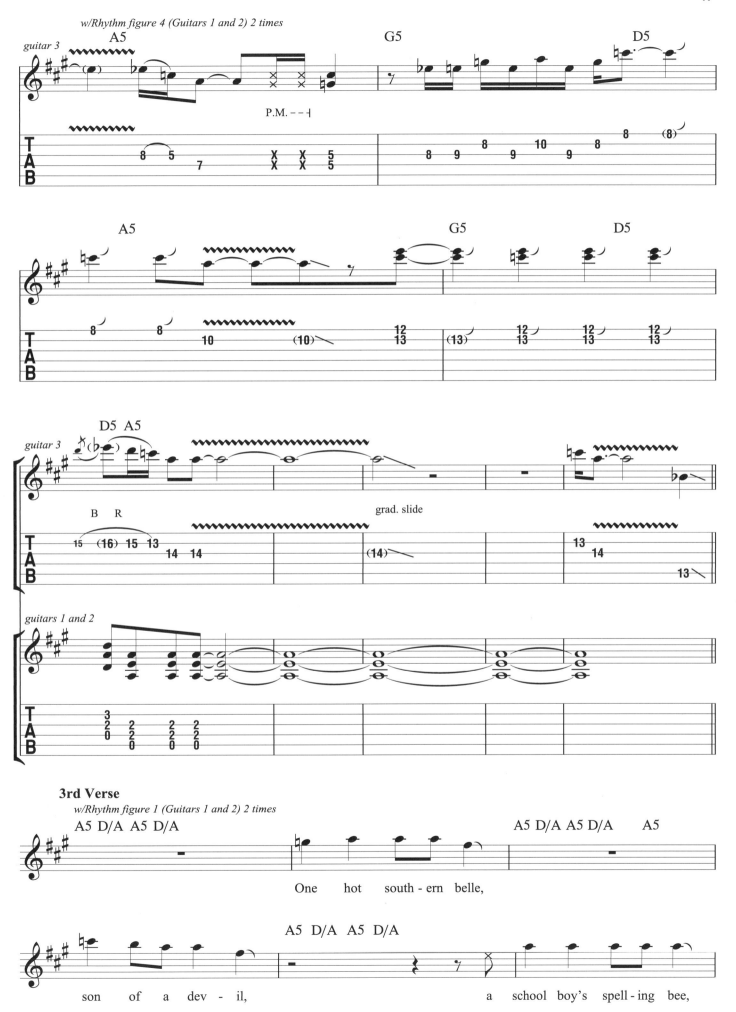

3rd Verse

w/Rhythm figure 1 (Guitars 1 and 2) 2 times

One hot south-ern belle,

son of a dev-il,

a school boy's spell-ing bee,

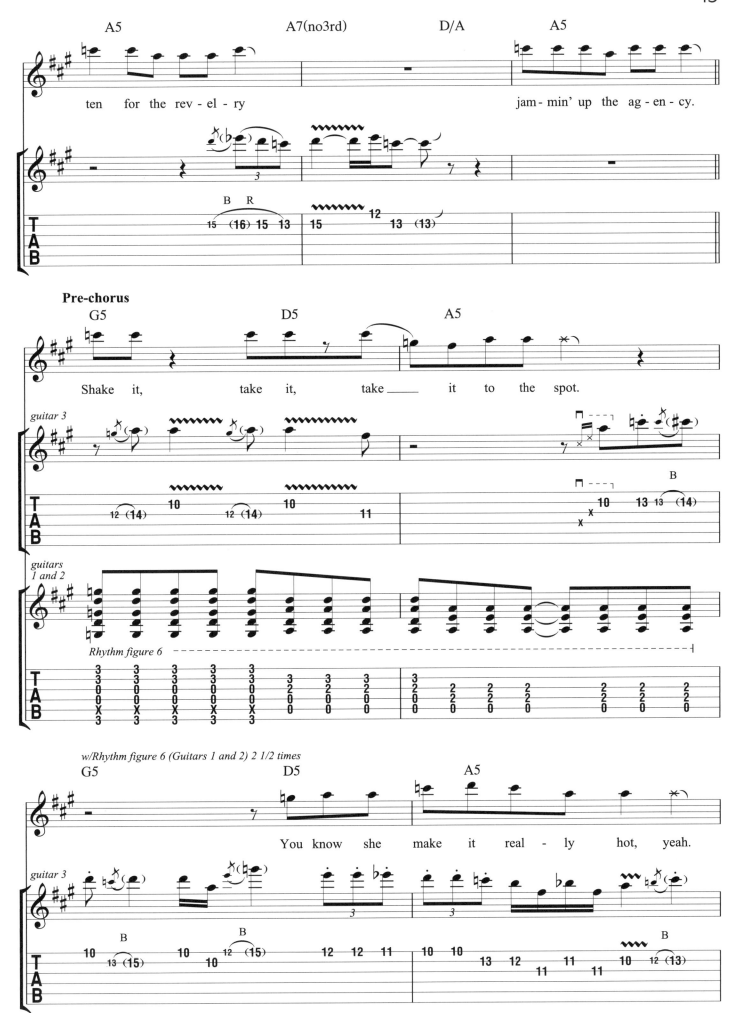

20

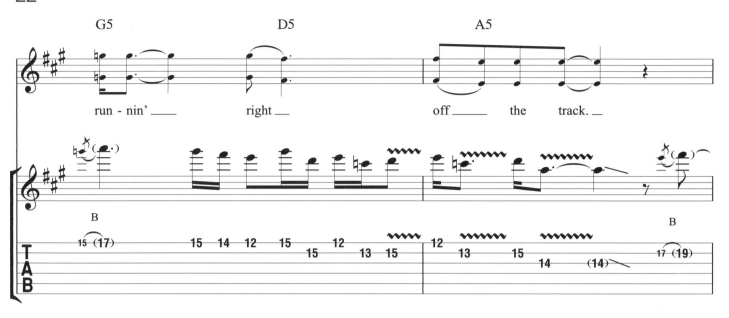

run - nin' ____ right ____ off ____ the track. ____

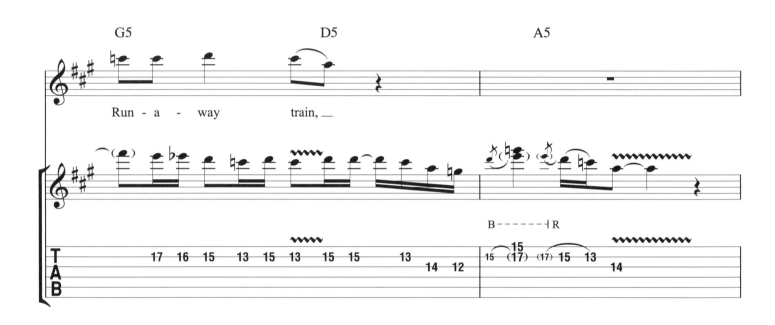

Run - a - way train, ____

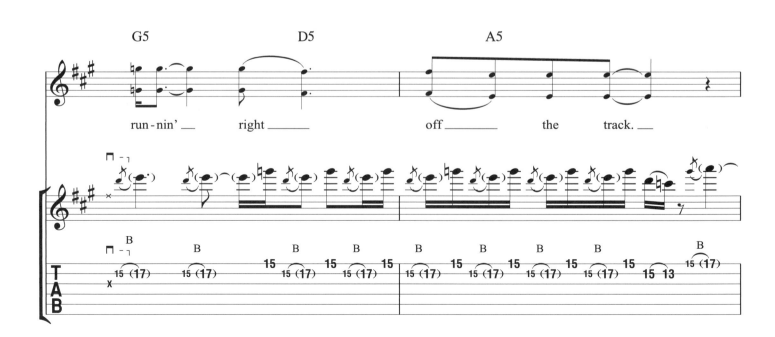

run - nin' ____ right ____ off ____ the track. ____

Additional lyrics

2nd Verse:
One hard ring a bell
Old school rebel
A ten for the revelry
Jamming up the agency

2nd Pre-Chorus:
Shake it, shake it
Take it to the spot
You know she made it really hot
Get it on, give it up
Come on give it all you got
Your mind on a fantasy
Living on the ecstasy

Skies On Fire

Words & Music by Angus Young & Malcolm Young

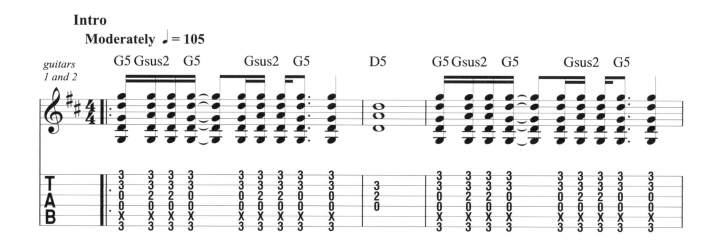

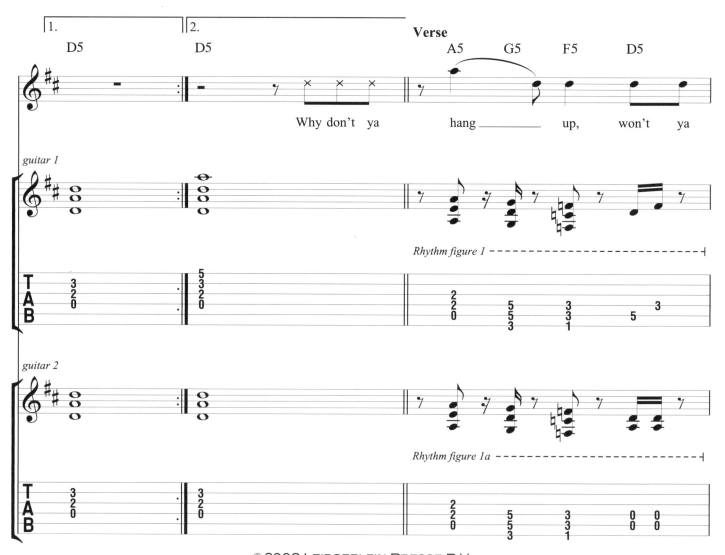

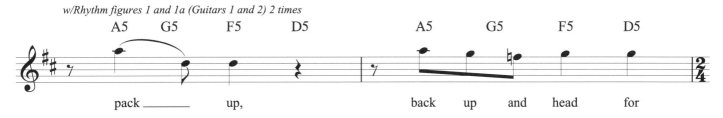

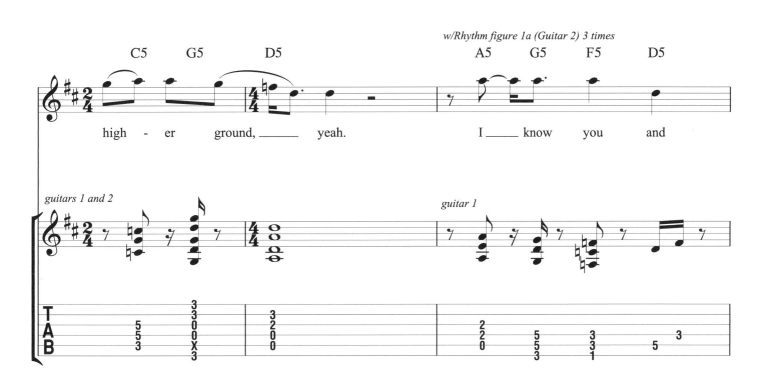

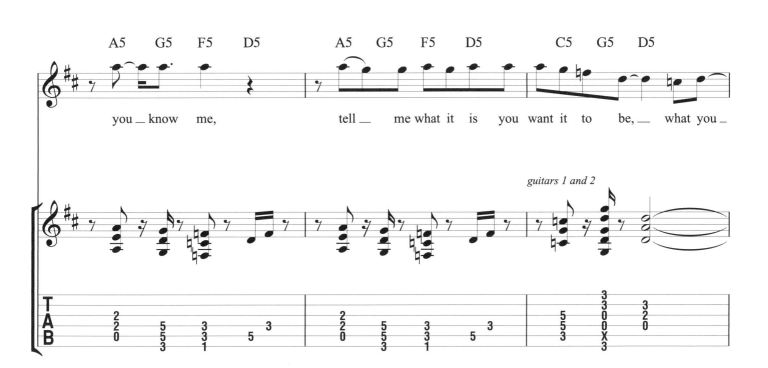

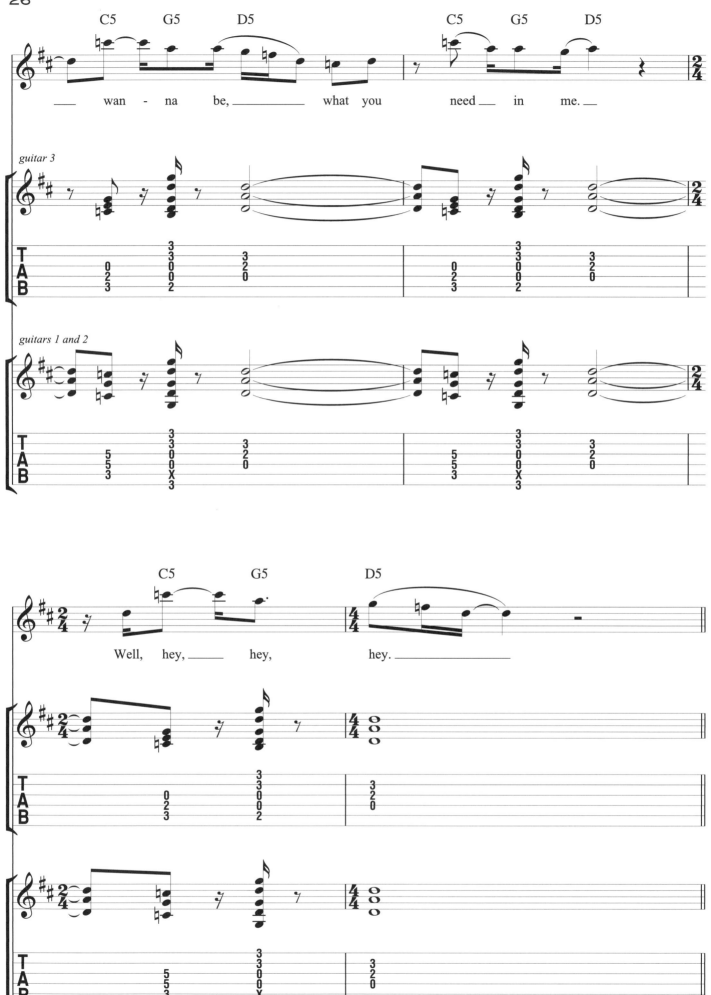

Chorus

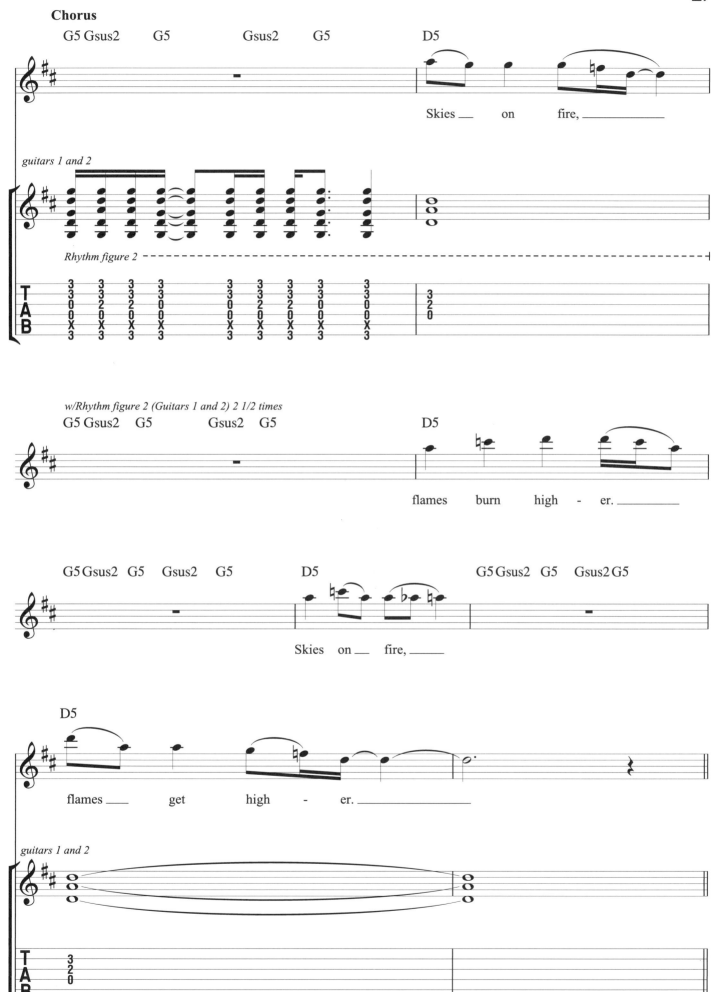

Verse

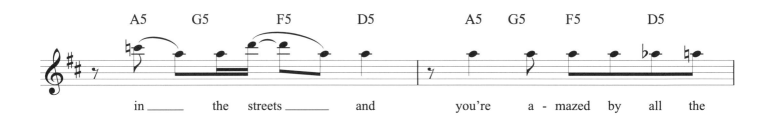

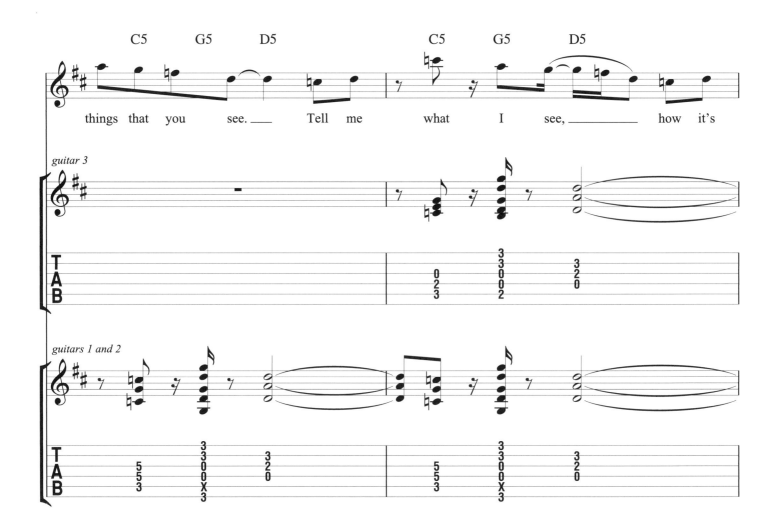

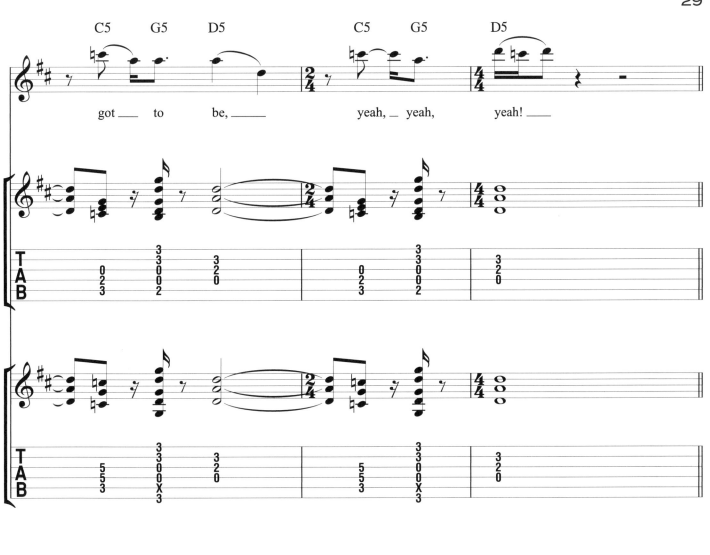

Chorus

w/Rhythm figure 2 (Guitars 1 and 2) 3 1/2 times

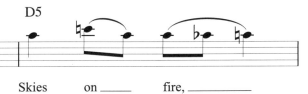

Skies on ____ fire, _____

flames burn high - er.

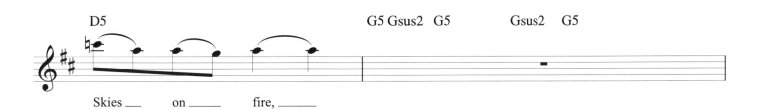

Skies ____ on ____ fire, ____

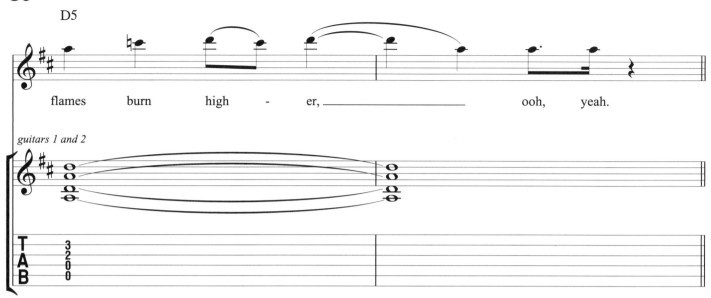

flames burn high - er, _____ ooh, yeah.

guitars 1 and 2

Guitar Solo

w/Rhythm figures 1 and 1a (Guitars 1 and 2) 7 times

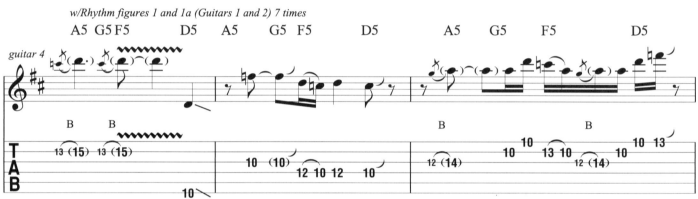

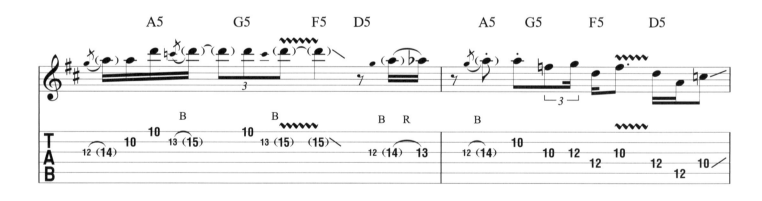

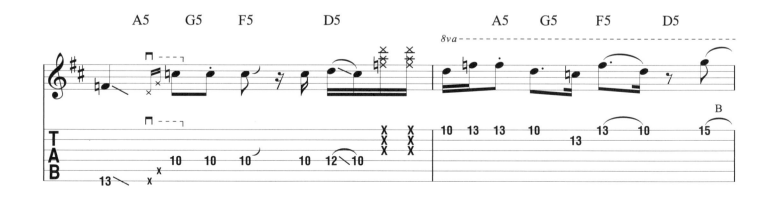

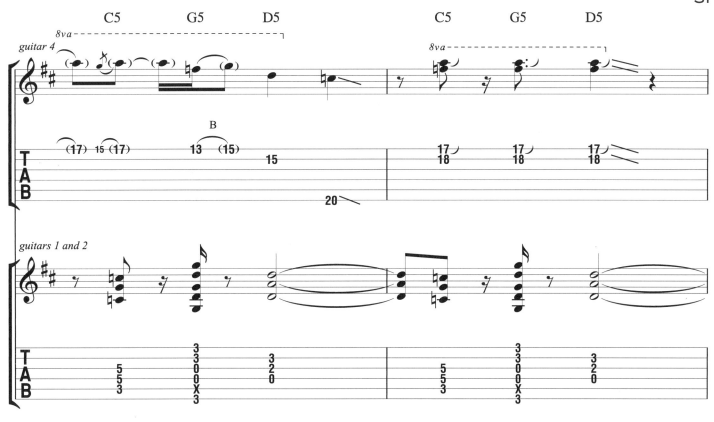

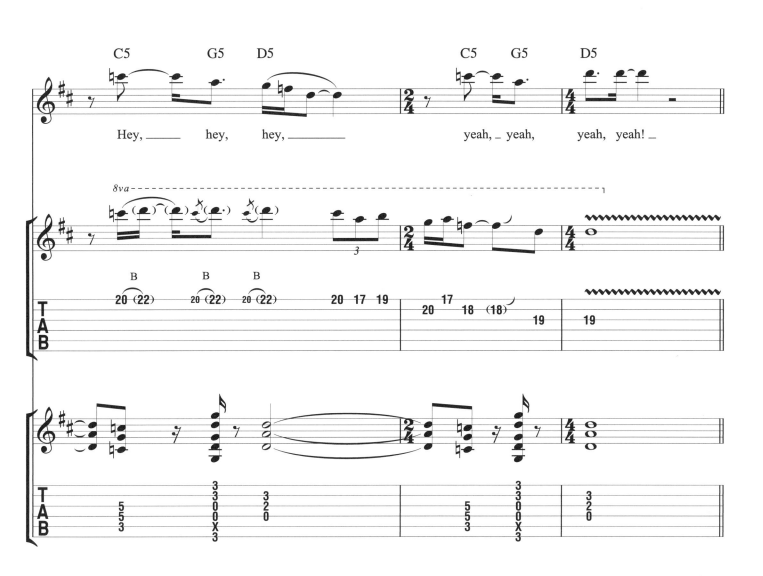

Hey, _____ hey, hey, _____ yeah, _ yeah, yeah, yeah! _

Chorus

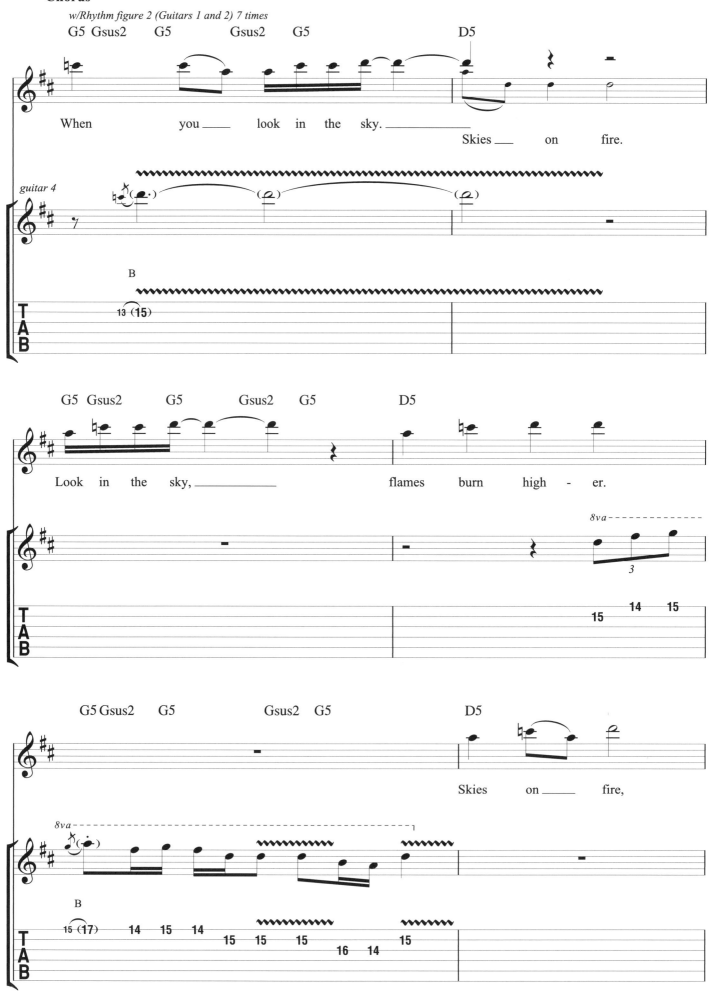

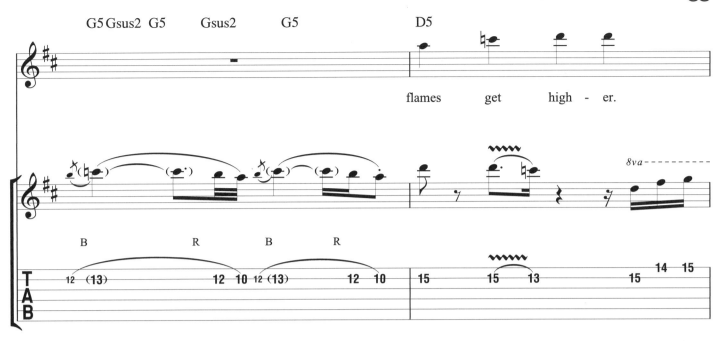

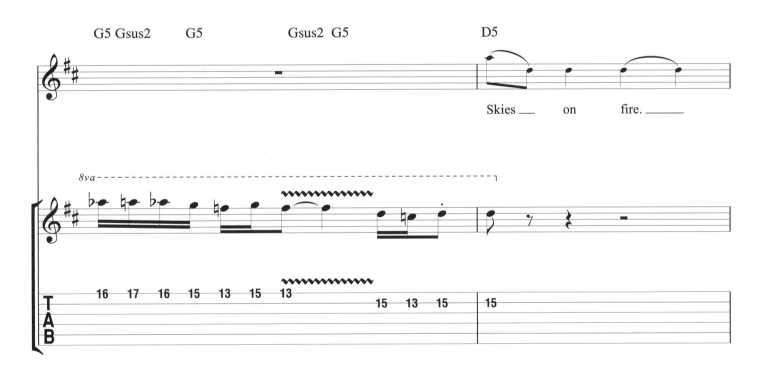

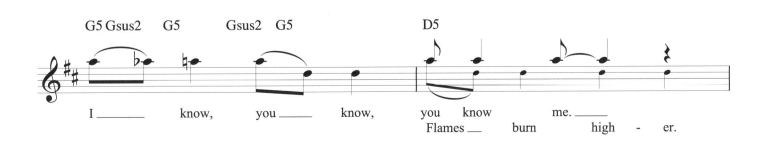

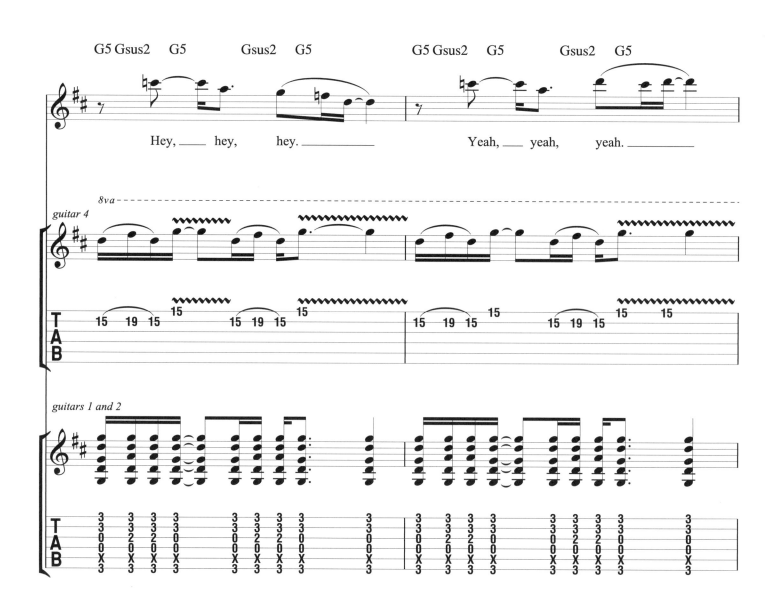

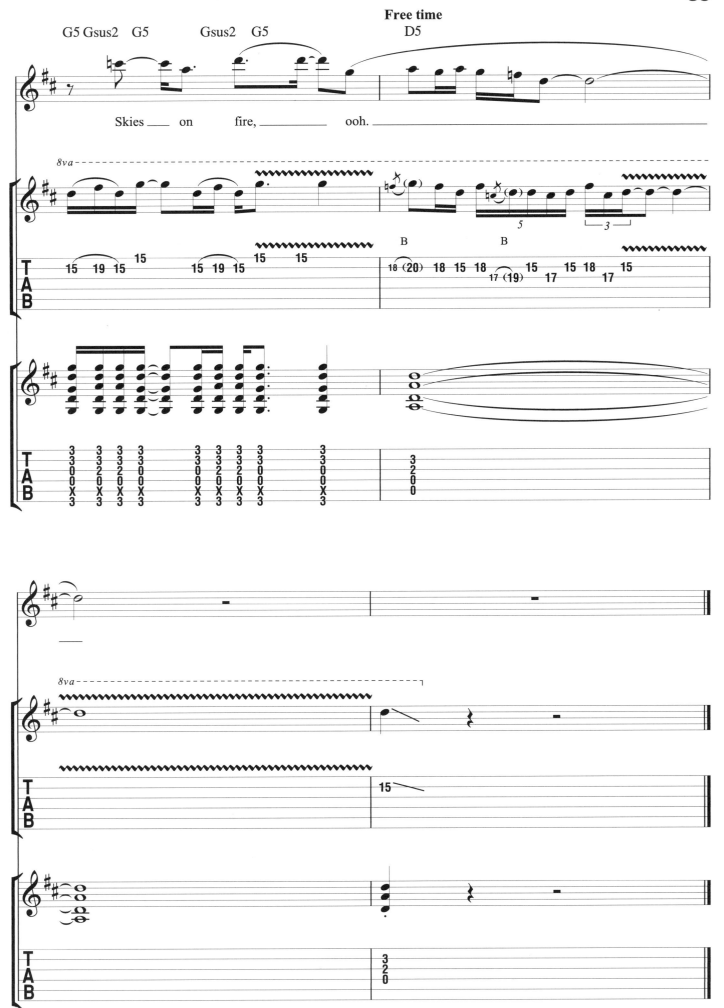

Anything Goes

Words & Music by Angus Young & Malcolm Young

Intro
Moderately ♩ = 120

(D5)

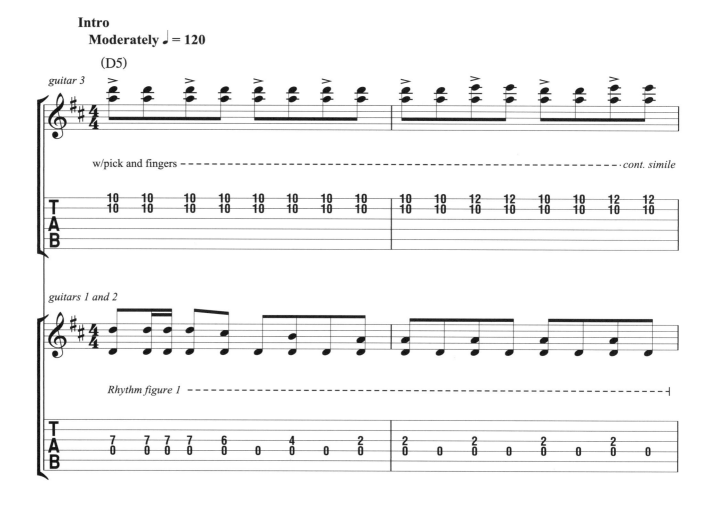

w/Rhythm figure 1 (Guitar 1) 3 times

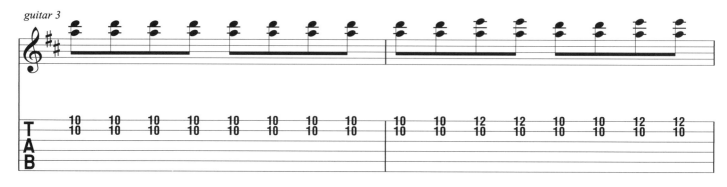

37

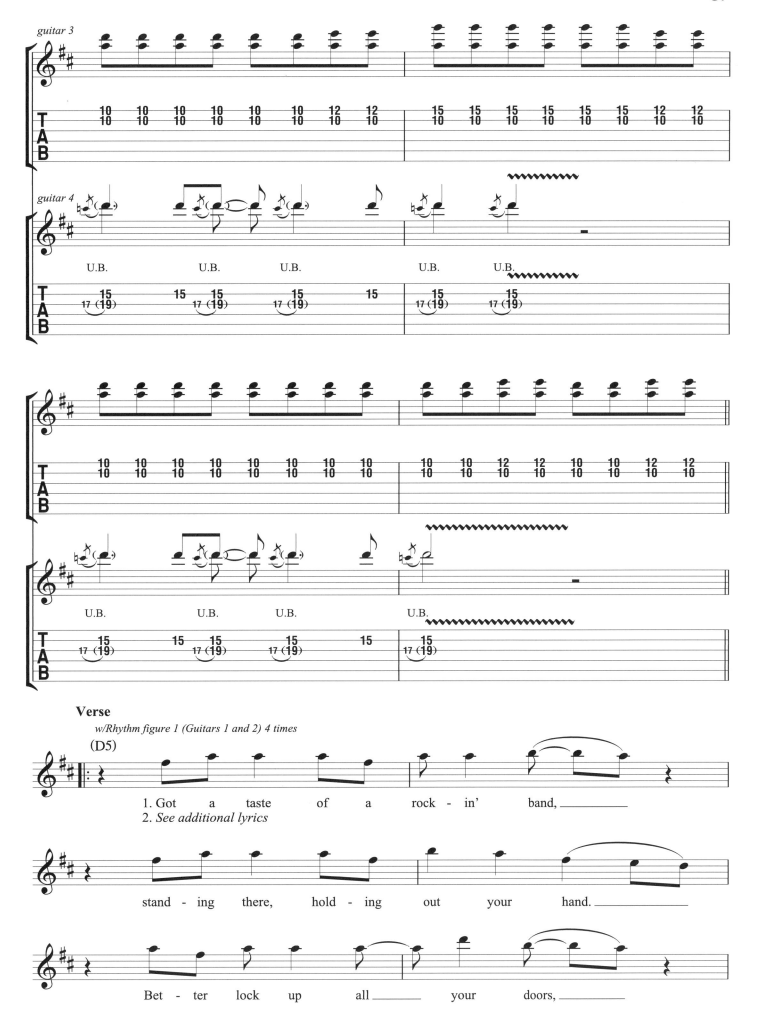

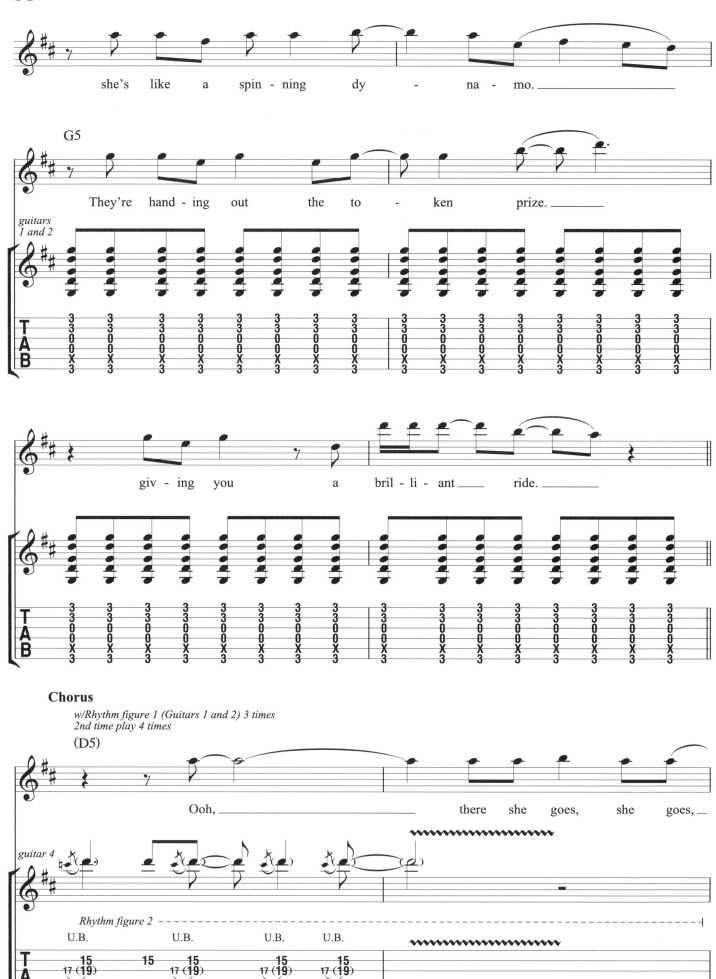

Chorus

and no - bod - y knows _

where she goes, she goes. ___

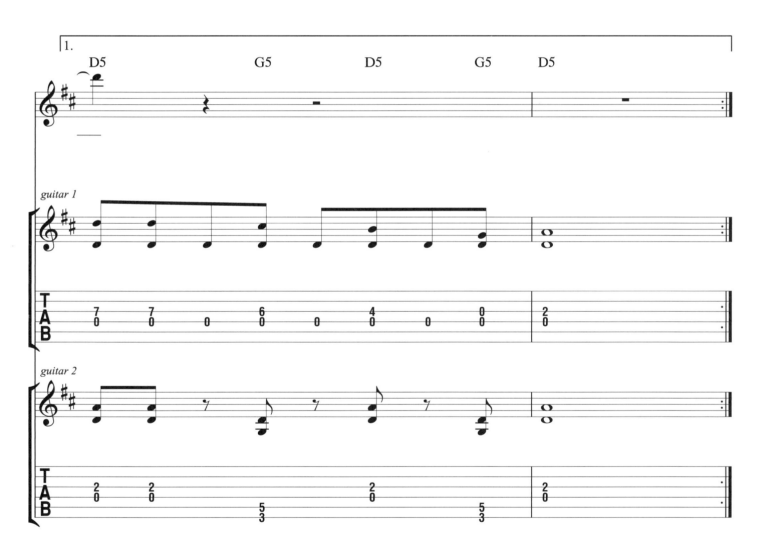

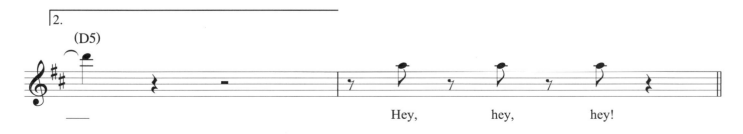

Hey, hey, hey!

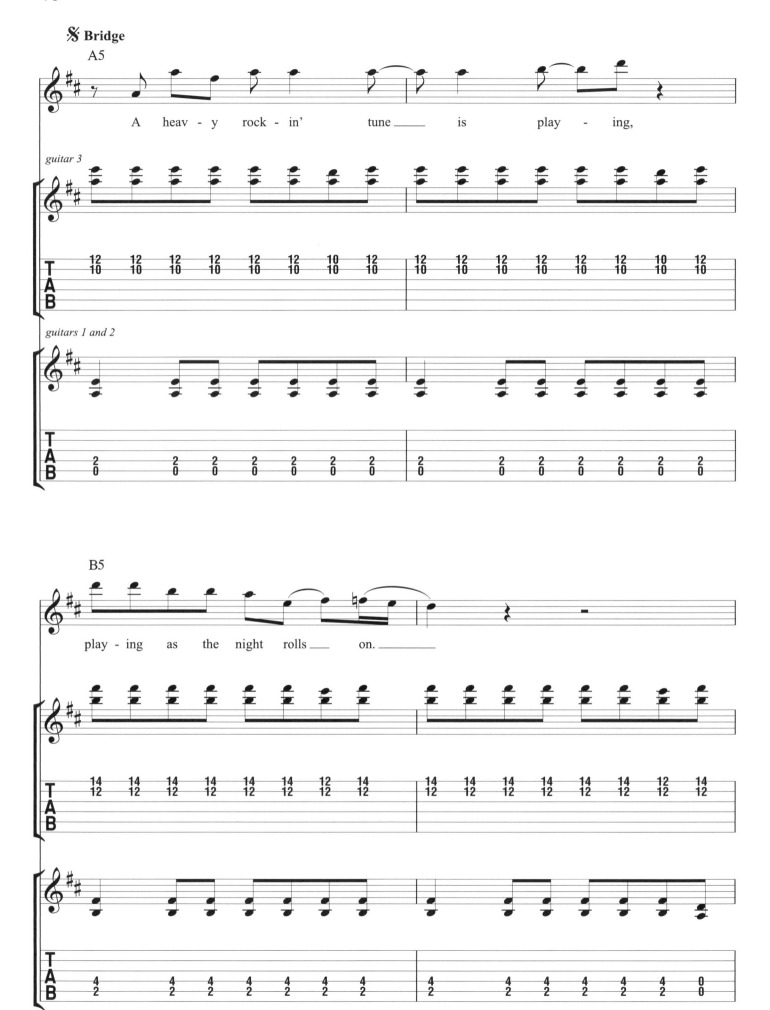

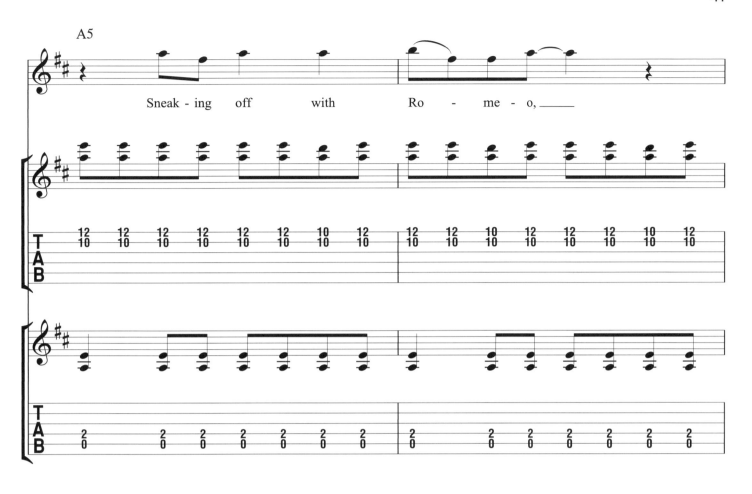

Sneak - ing off with Ro - me - o, _____

To Coda ⊕

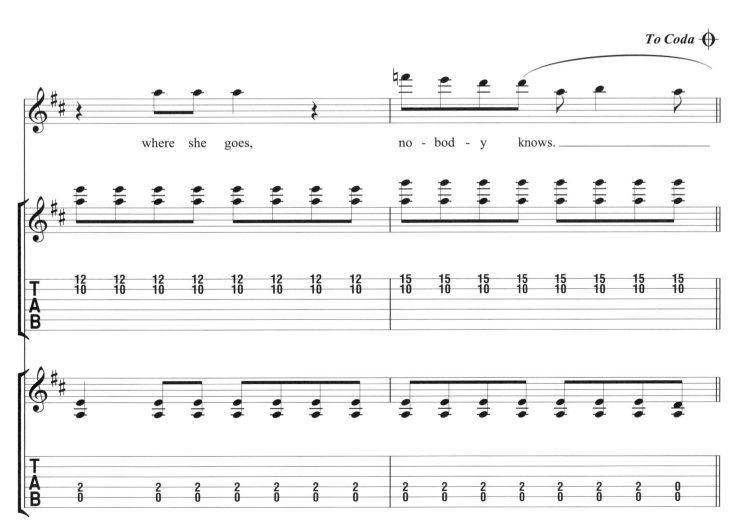

where she goes, no - bod - y knows. _____

Guitar Solo

w/Rhythm figure 1 (Guitars 1 and 2) 2 times

(D5)

G5

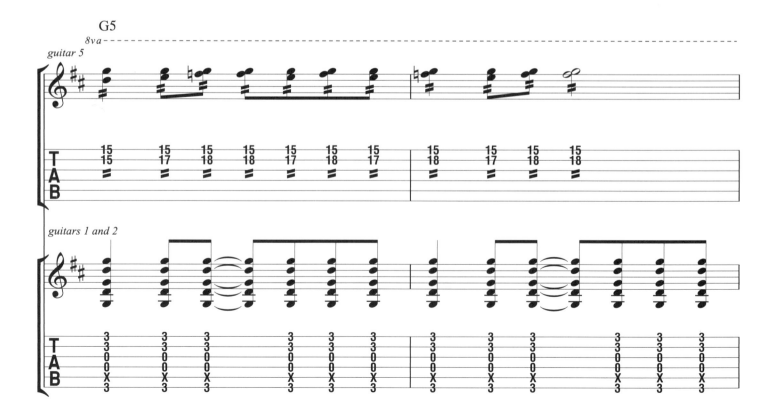

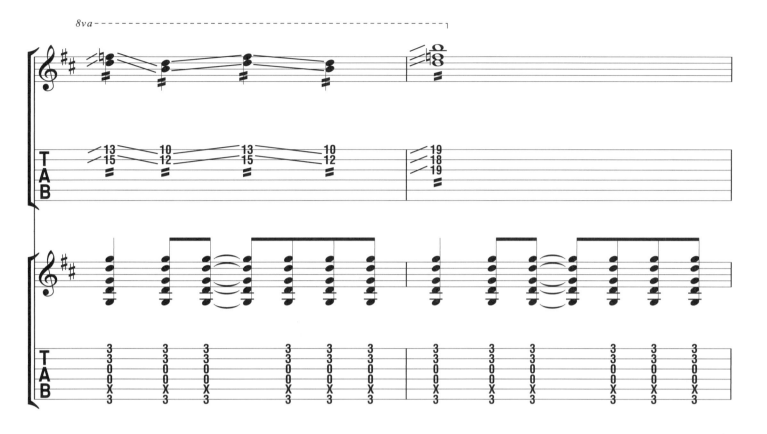

w/Rhythm figure 1 (Guitars 1 and 2) 2 times

D5

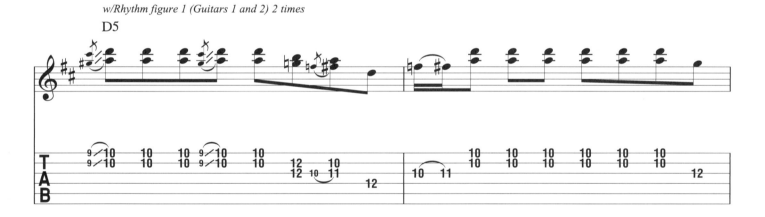

D.S. 𝄋 al Coda ⊕

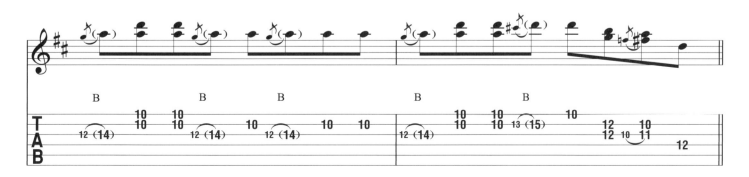

44

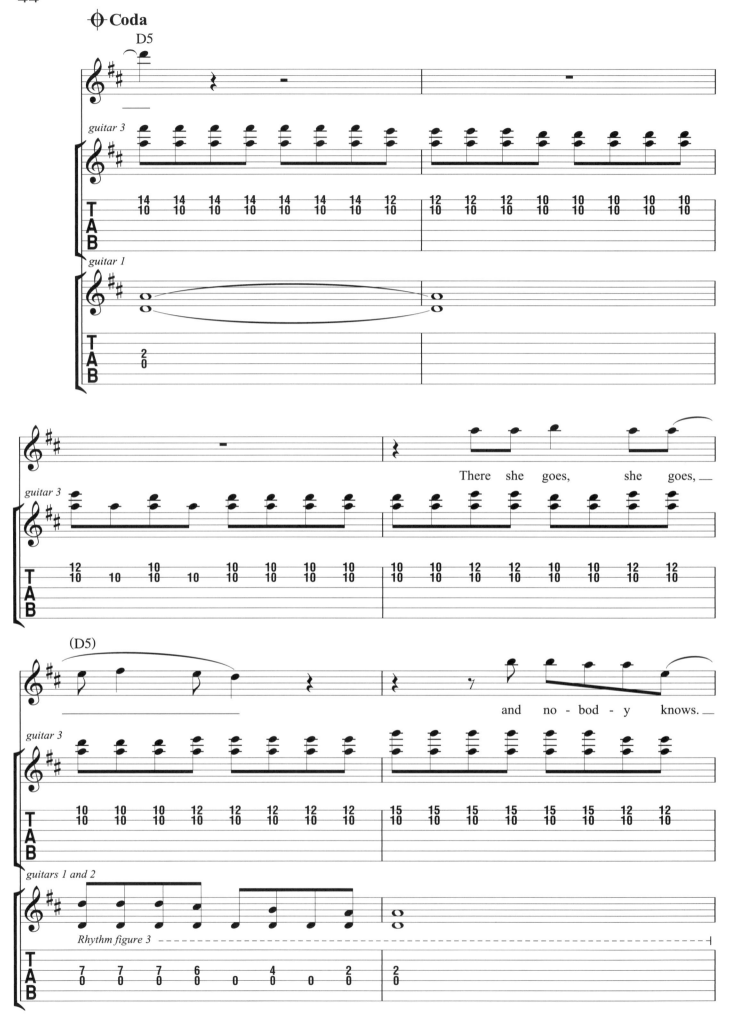

There she goes, she goes, ___

and no - bod - y knows.

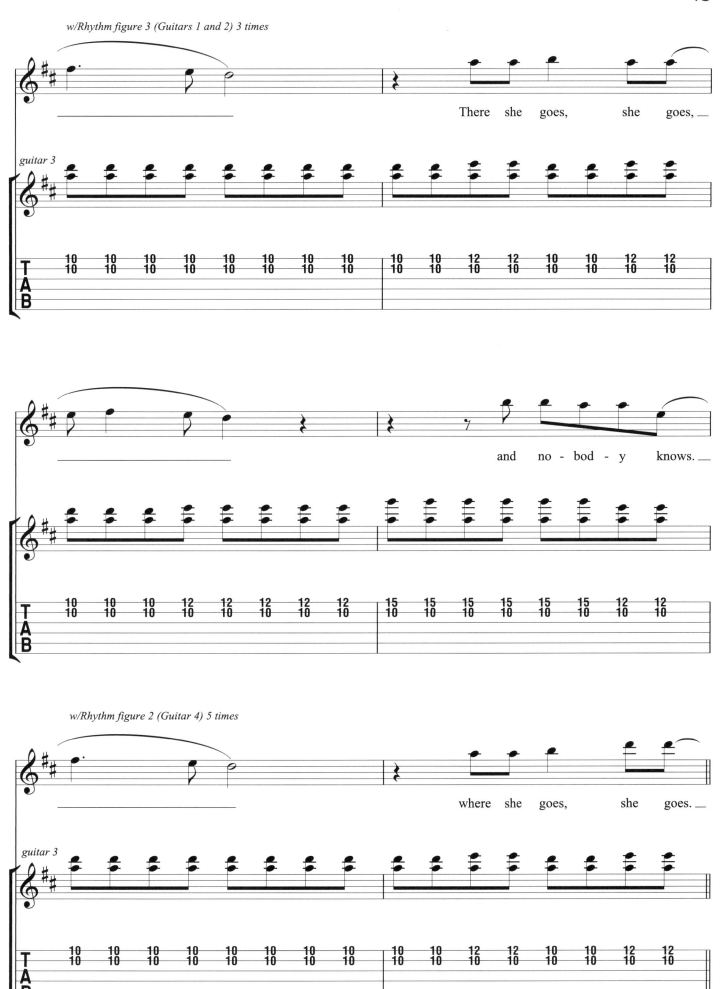

Outro

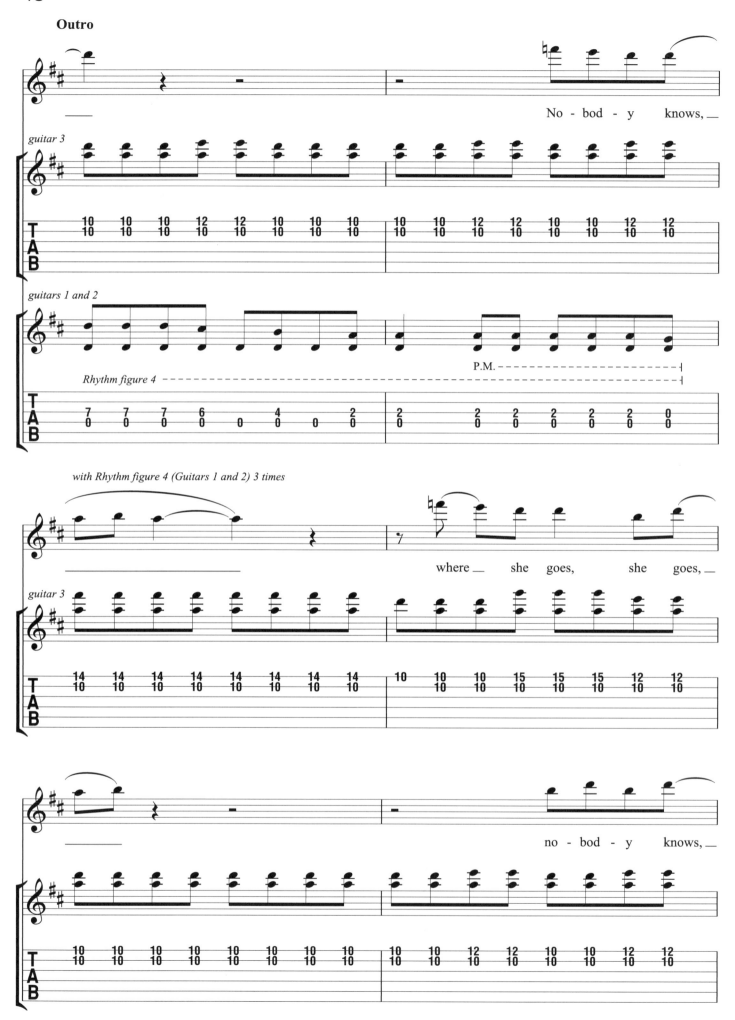

where she goes, ___ she goes. ___

Additional lyrics

2nd Verse:
Bangin' drums, workin' on all fours
A heavy tune I can play you loud
You know she's blown away all the others
You're never man enough to take it on all night
You better razzle-dazzle on that stage
Keep rockin' on all through the night

2nd Bridge:
A heavy rockin' tune is playing
On a flat, new color T.V.
Sneaking over creepy-crawlies
Never give it up
To take it on through the night

War Machine

Words & Music by Angus Young & Malcolm Young

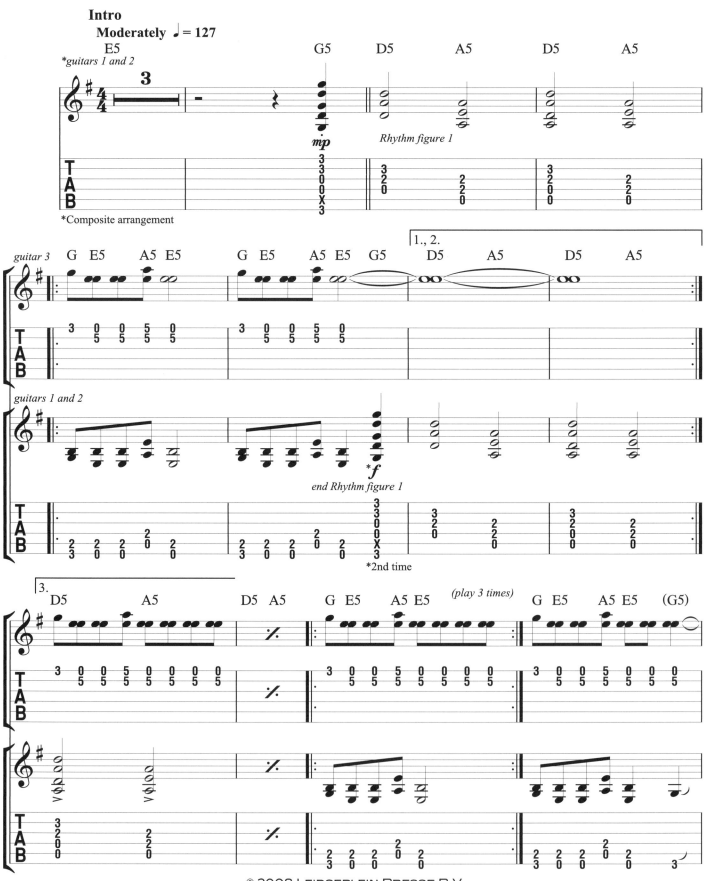

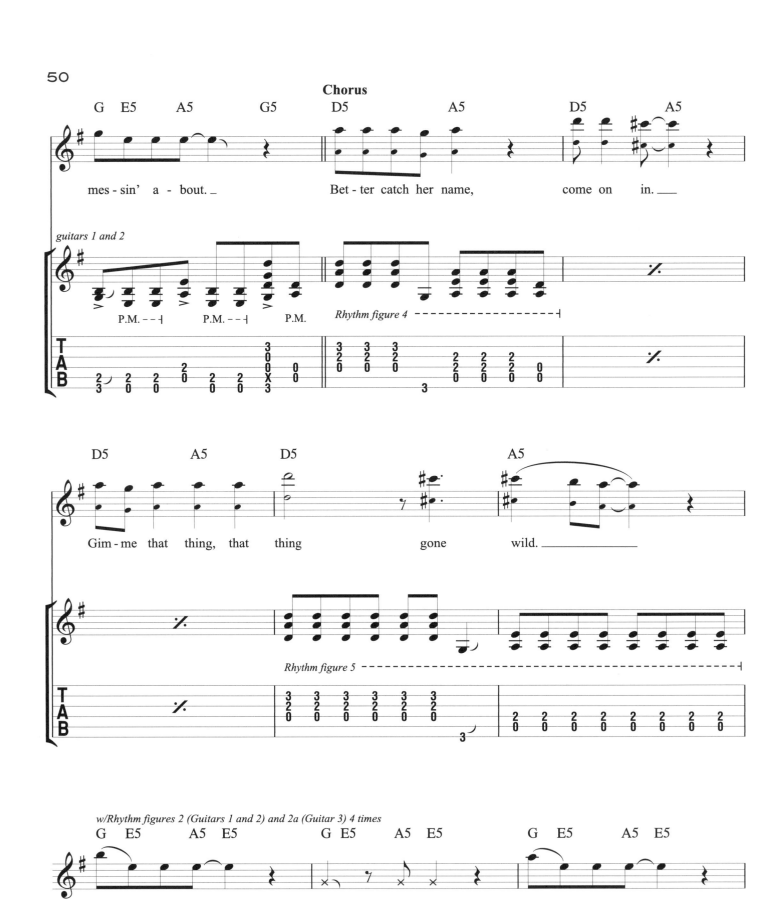

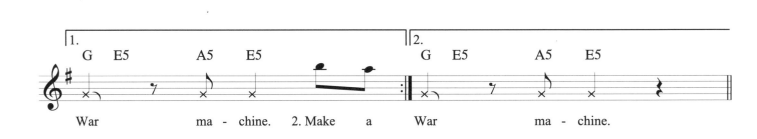

Breakdown

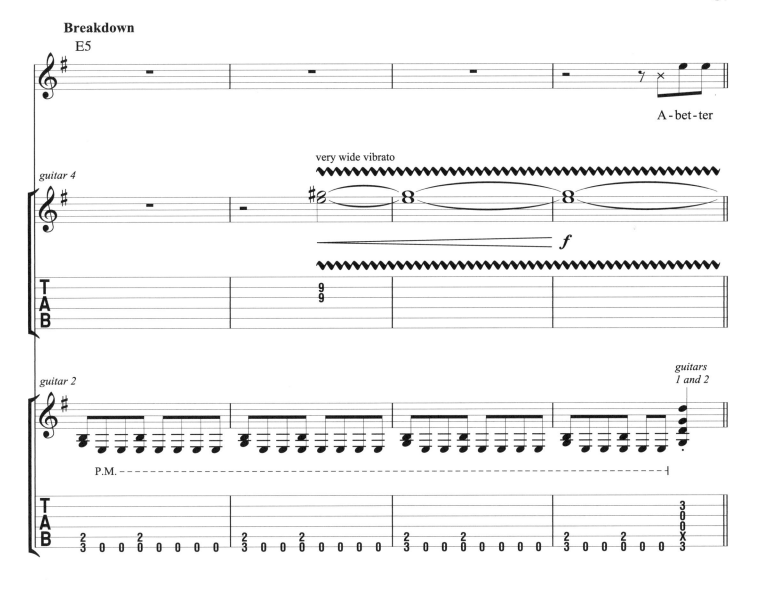

A - bet - ter

Bridge

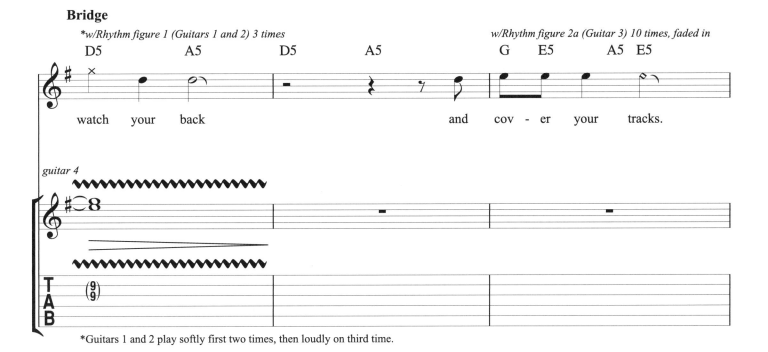

watch your back

and cov - er your tracks.

*Guitars 1 and 2 play softly first two times, then loudly on third time.

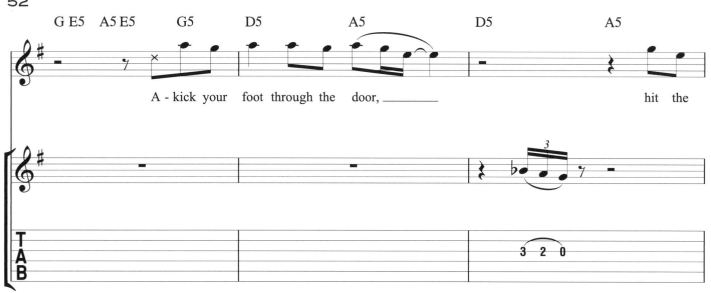

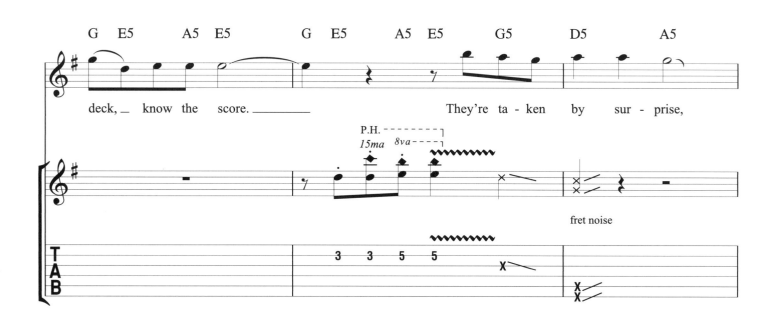

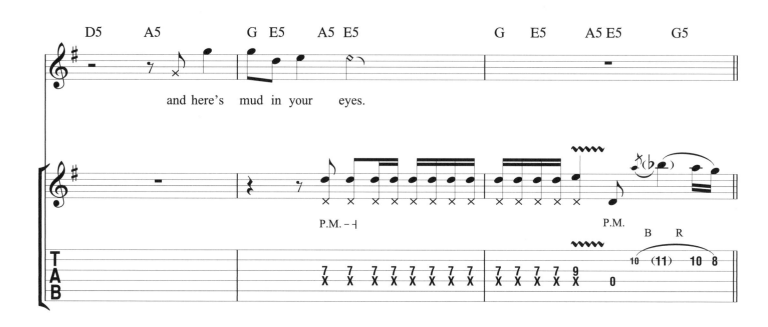

Chorus

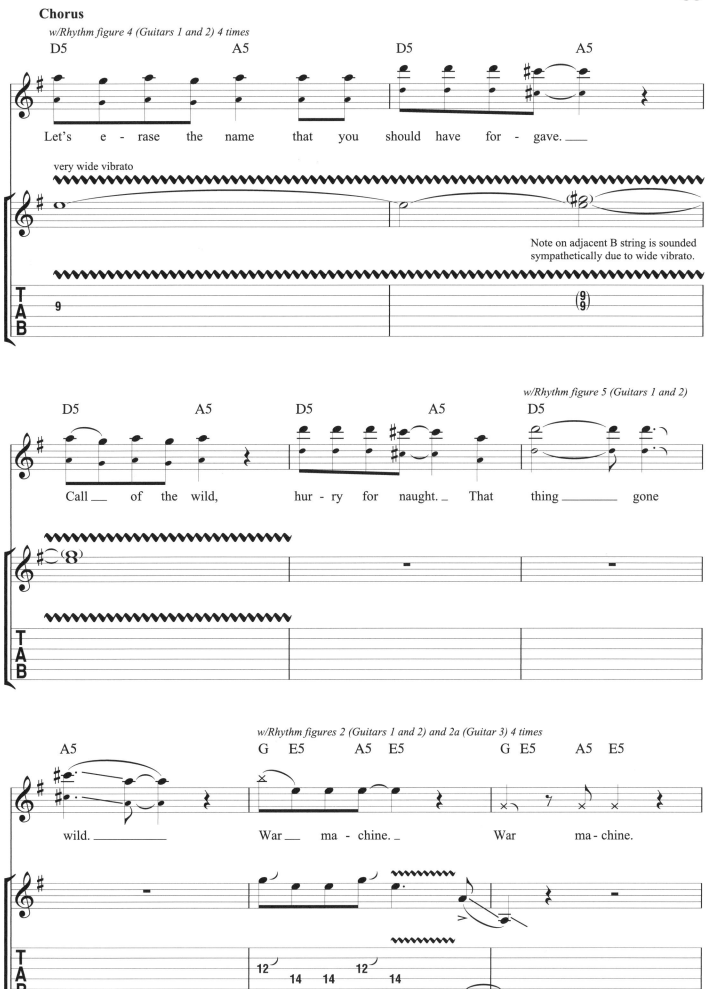

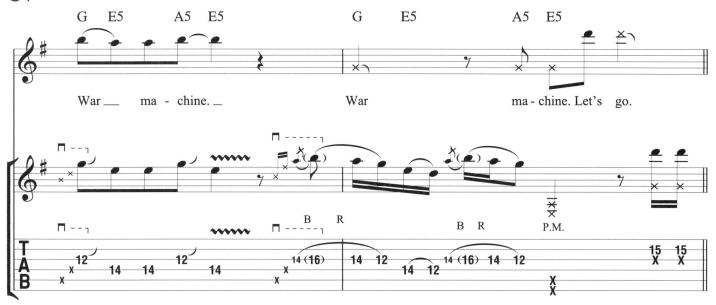

War __ ma - chine. __   War   ma - chine. Let's   go.

Outro Guitar Solo

w/Rhythm figure 4 (Guitars 1 and 2) 4 times

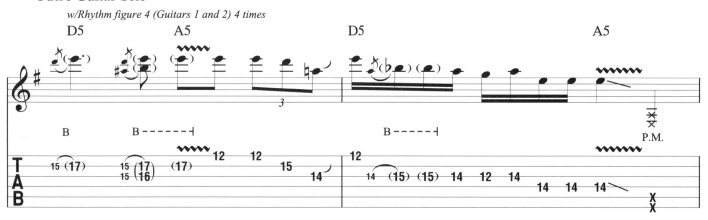

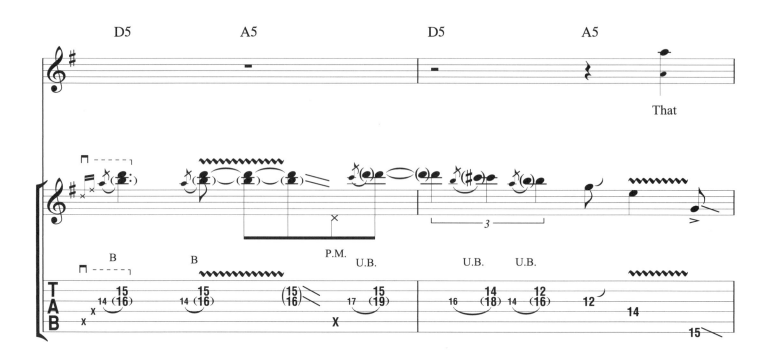

That

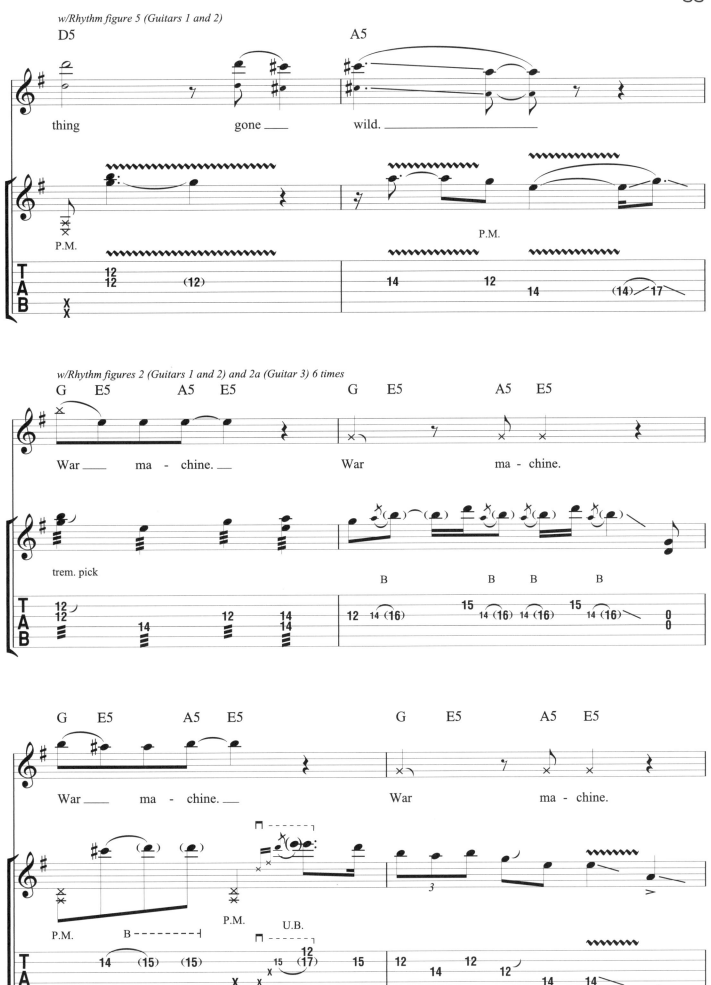

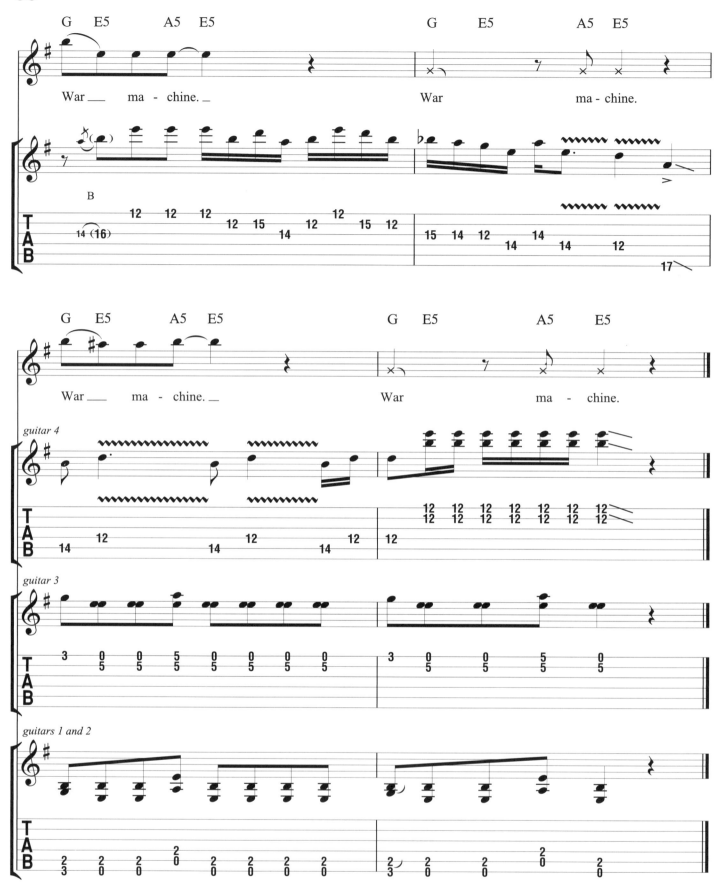

Additional lyrics

2nd Verse:
Make a stand, show your hand
Call in the high command
Don't think, just obey
I'm like a bird of prey

Big Jack

Words & Music by Angus Young & Malcolm Young

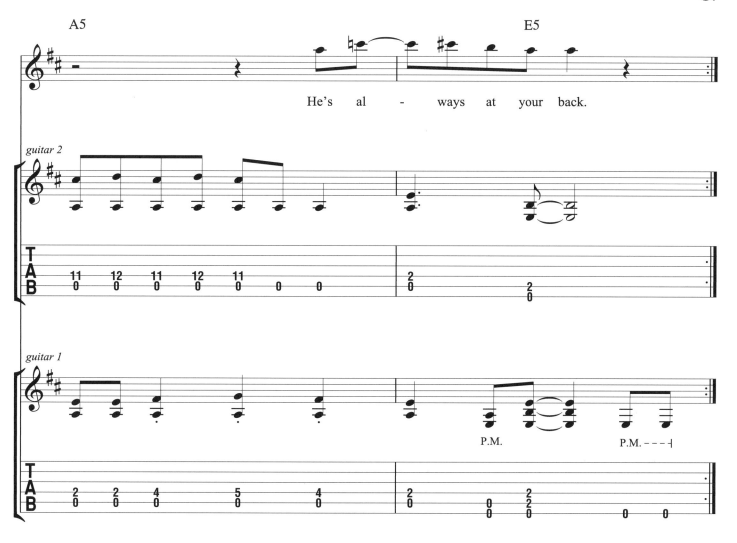

He's al - ways at your back.

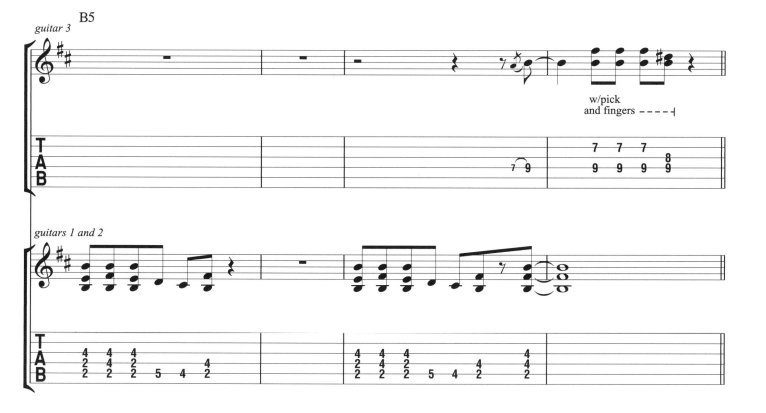

Guitar Solo

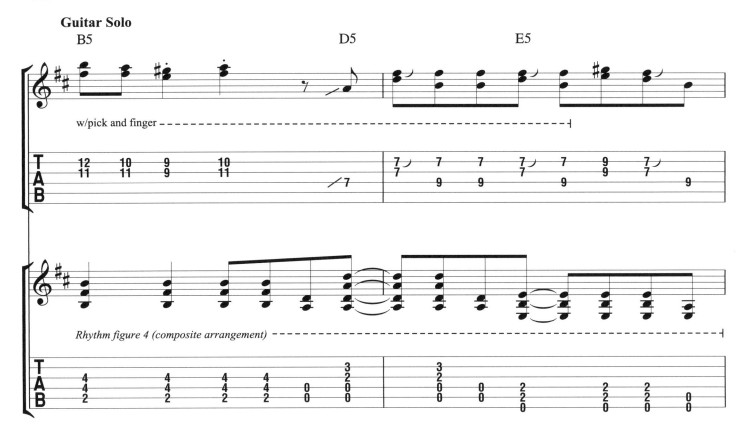

w/Rhythm figure 4 (Guitars 1 and 2) 2 times

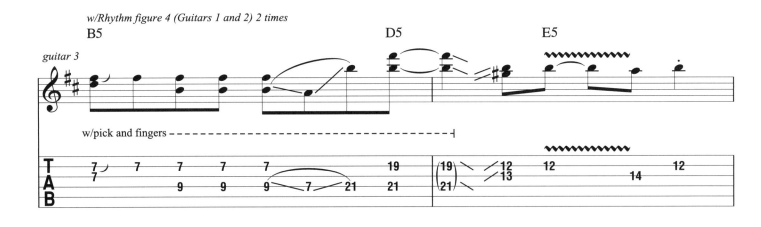

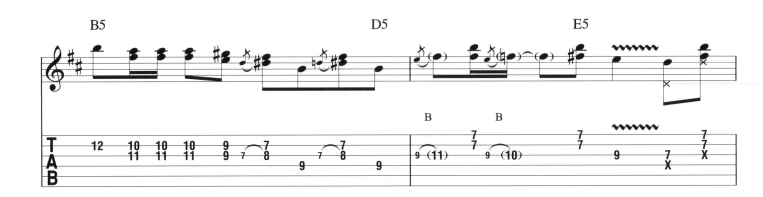

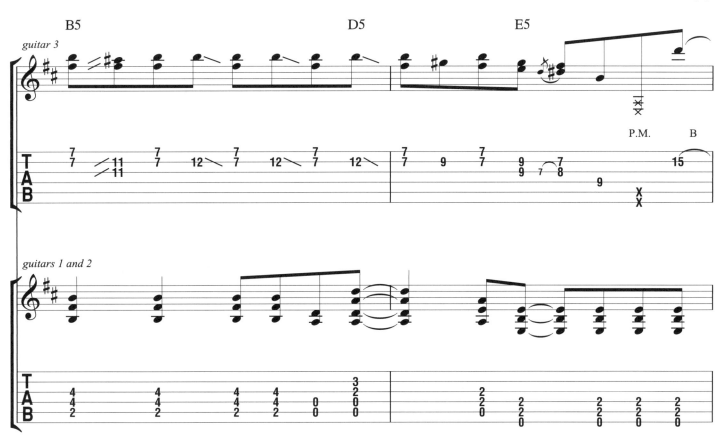

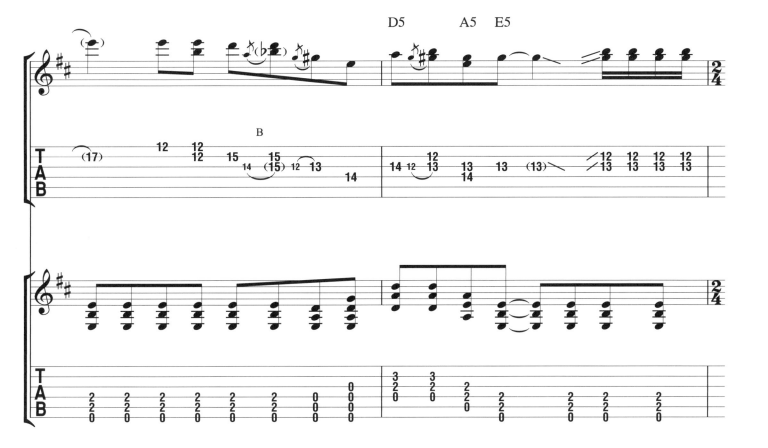

D.S. 𝄋 al Coda ⊕

Ⓞ Coda

Ain't no need to wor - ry, he's al - ways got your back.

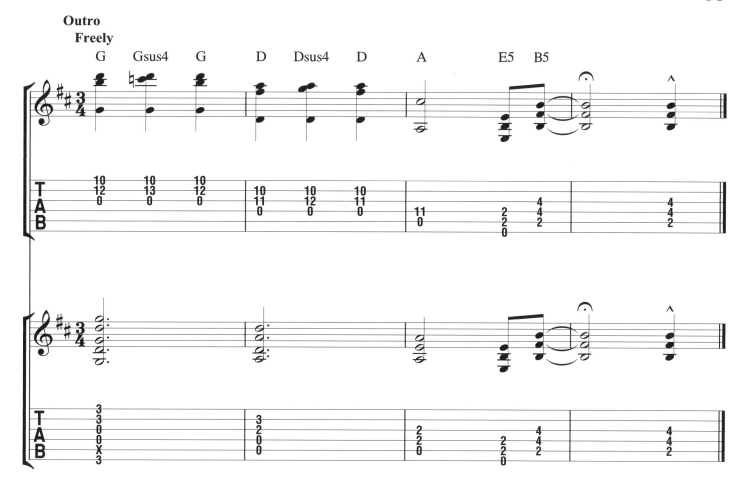

Additional lyrics

2nd Verse:
You never leave a dollar, racking up the balls
You like to get it on fast, back there standing tall
When he hears the siren, he's gonna put you on the racks
He's got a bad reputation, climbing all over the bars

2nd Pre-Chorus:
Gonna press the flesh
Rockin' rollin' soldier
He's the last of them all
Well, tell Jack, he's on his way

2nd Chorus:
Big Jack, Big Jack
You know it's only natural to get you up to scratch
Big Jack, Big Jack
Always into trouble, got to turn the other way
Big Jack, Big Jack
Always likes to party and he likes the girls to play
Big Jack, look out, Jack
He's always at your back

Smash N Grab

Words & Music by Angus Young & Malcolm Young

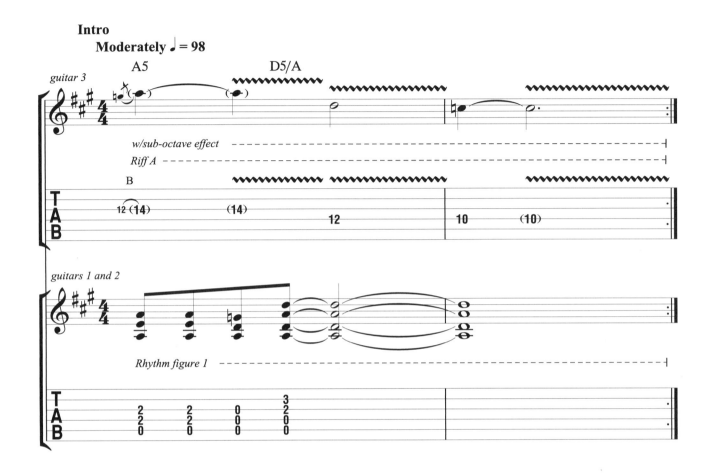

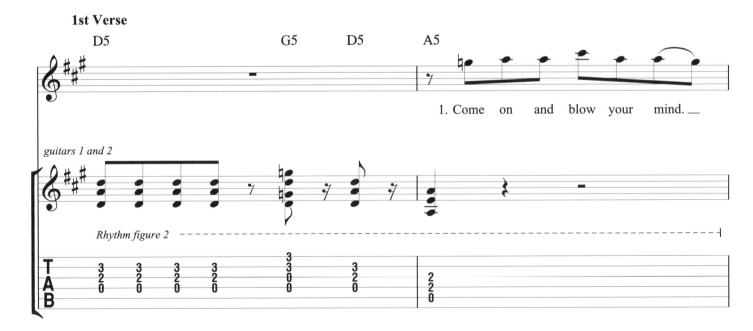

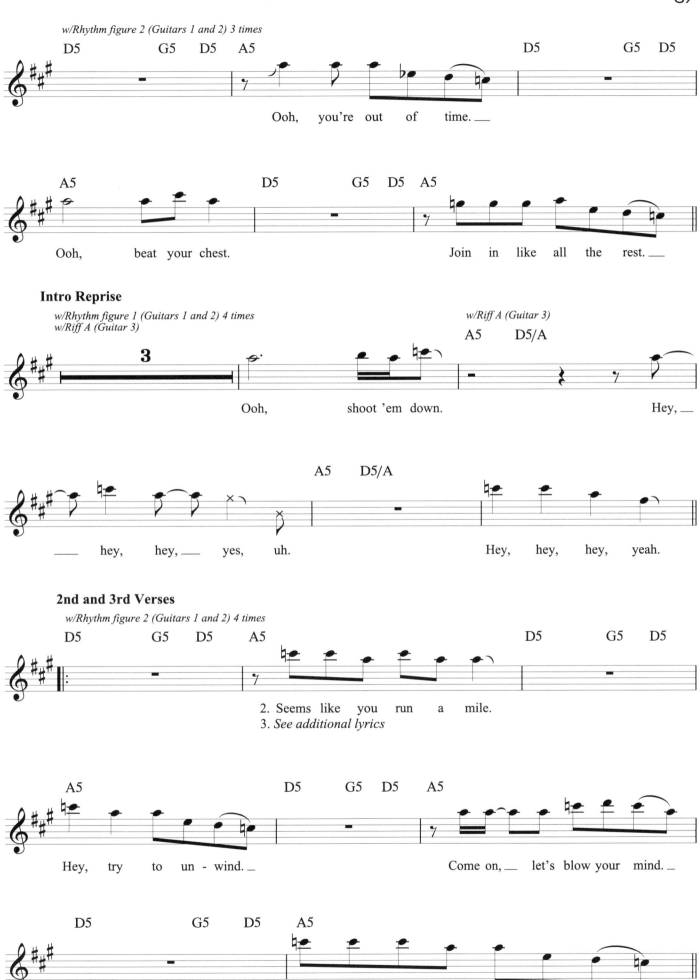

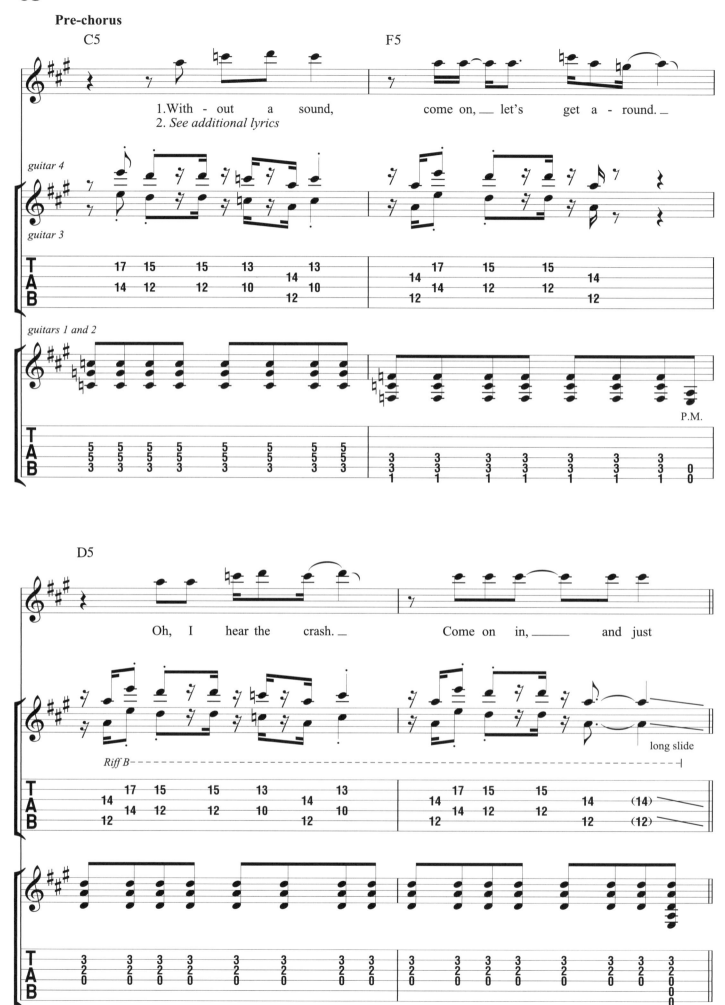

Chorus

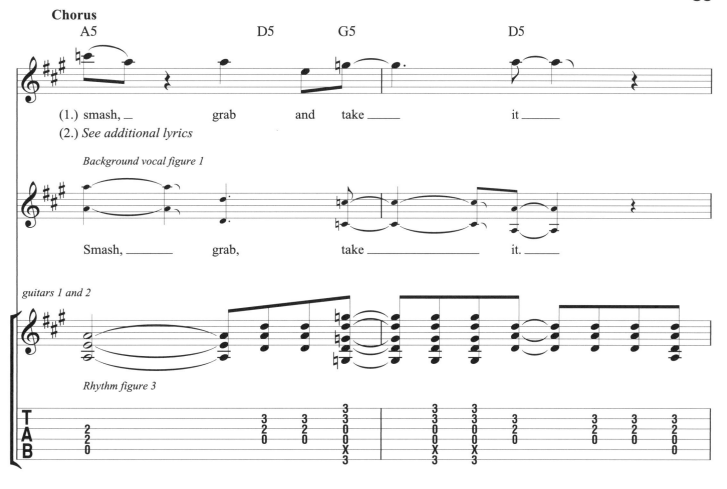

(1.) smash, ___ grab and take _____ it _____

(2.) *See additional lyrics*

Background vocal figure 1

Smash, _____ grab, take _____ it. ___

guitars 1 and 2

Rhythm figure 3

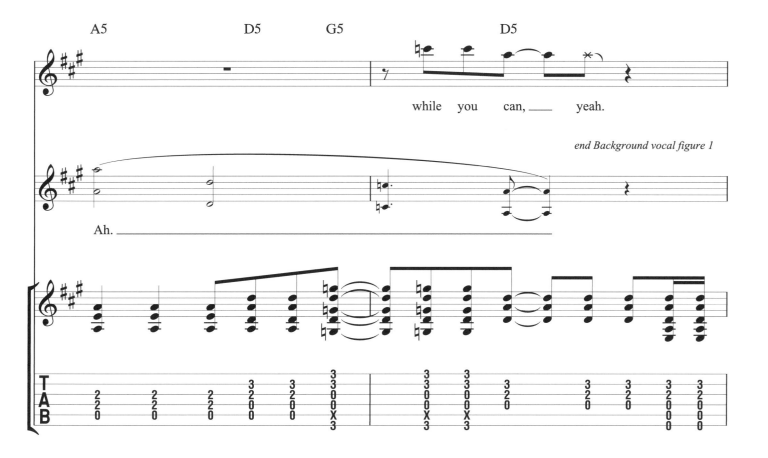

while you can, ___ yeah.

end Background vocal figure 1

Ah. _____

70

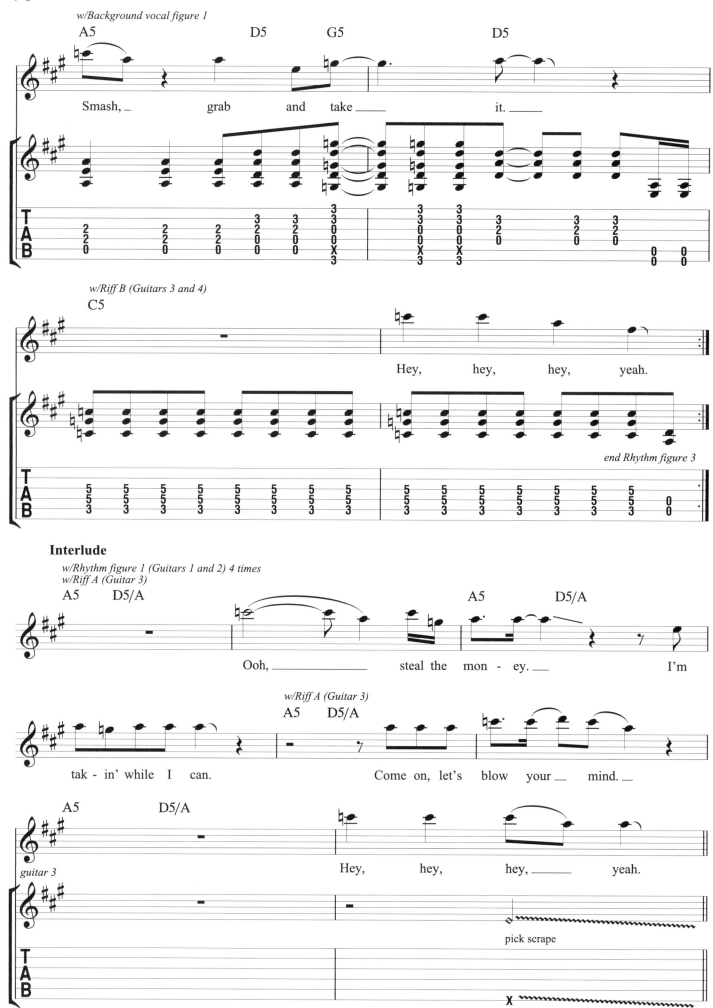

Guitar Solo

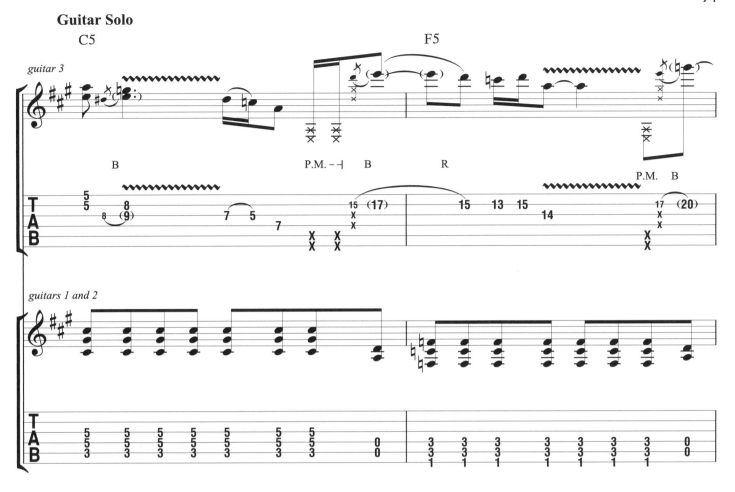

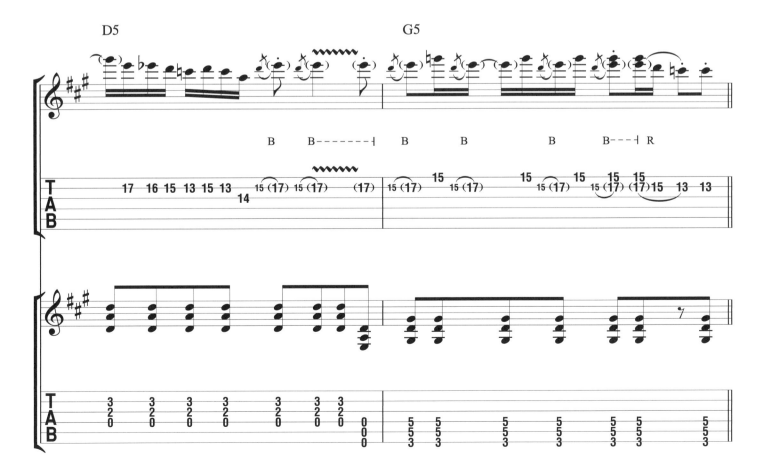

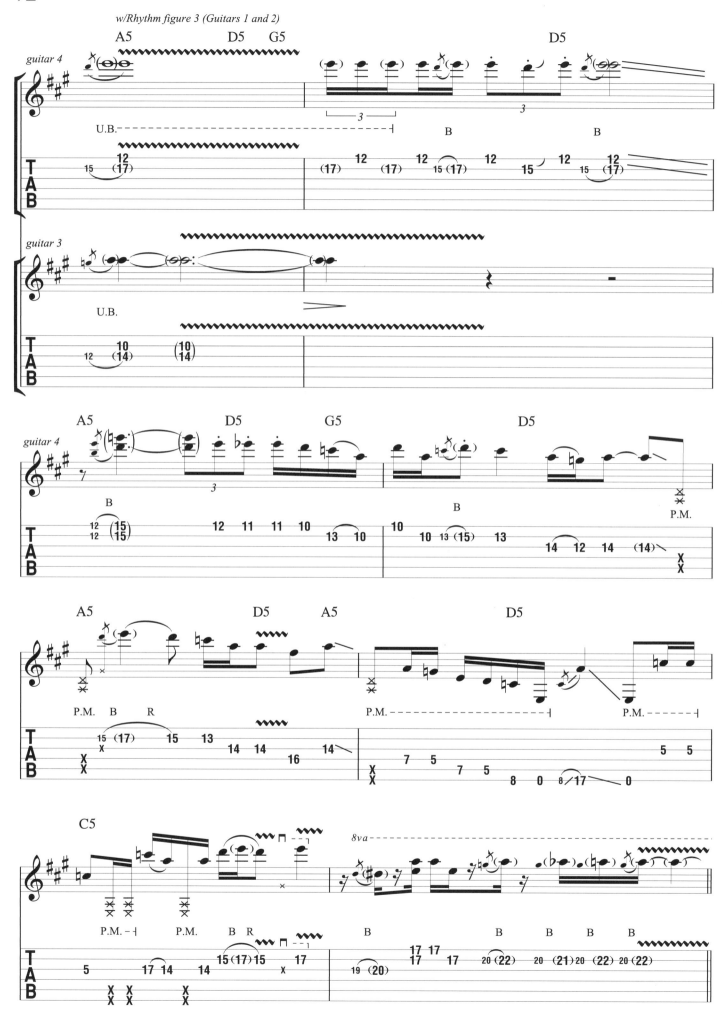

Breakdown

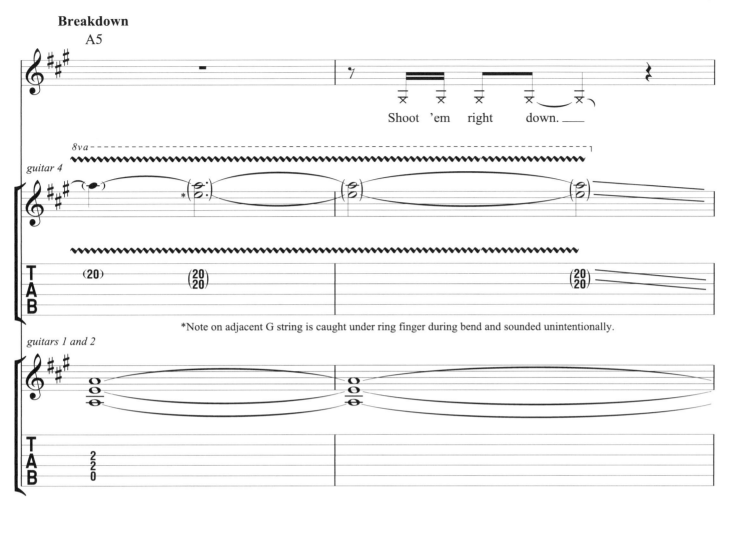

Shoot 'em right down. ___

Note on adjacent G string is caught under ring finger during bend and sounded unintentionally.

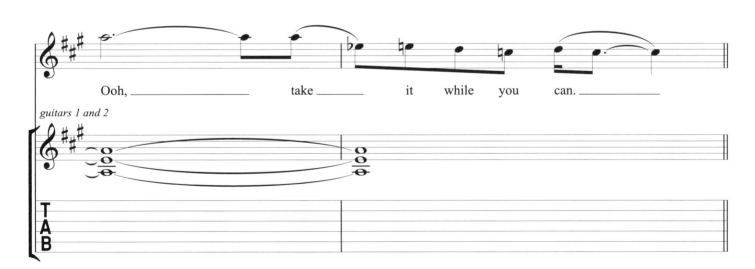

Ooh, ___ take ___ it while you can. ___

Outro Chorus

w/Rhythm figure 1 (Guitars 1 and 2) 7 times
w/Riff A (Guitar 3)

Come on, let's ___ blow ___ your mind.

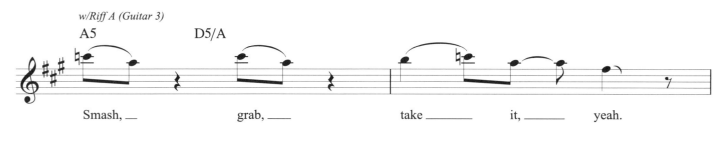

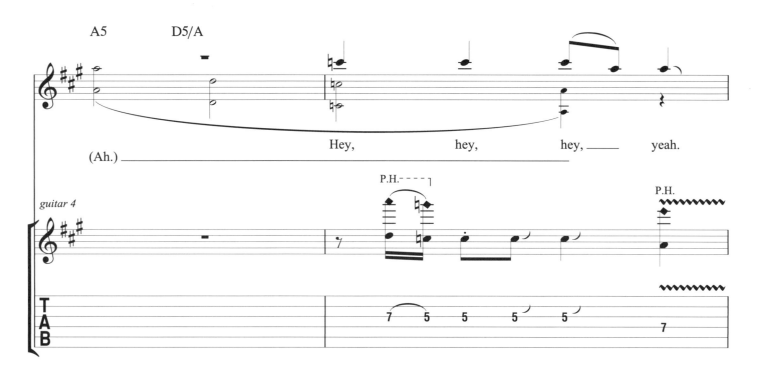

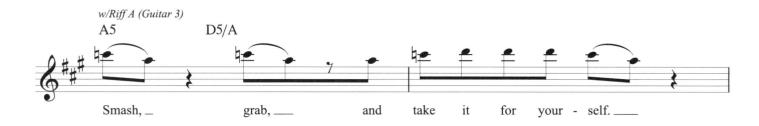

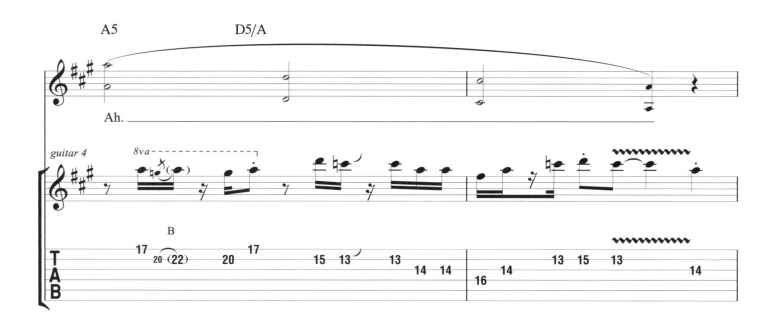

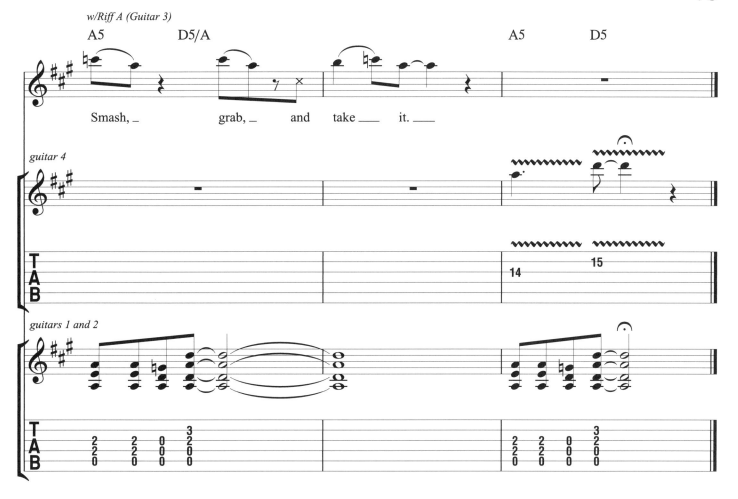

Smash, _ grab, _ and take ___ it. ___

3rd Verse:
Why don't you come out?
Come on, run it to the ground
You're gonna blow your mind
You're gonna pulverize

2nd Pre-Chorus:
Once you've come up late
You gotta pick up straight
It's gonna blow your mind
And all the living's gone

2nd Chorus:
Smash, grab and take it
Take it for yourself
Smash, grab and take it
Take it, take it, take it, yeah

Spoilin' For A Fight

Words & Music by Angus Young & Malcolm Young

Intro
Moderately ♩ = 124

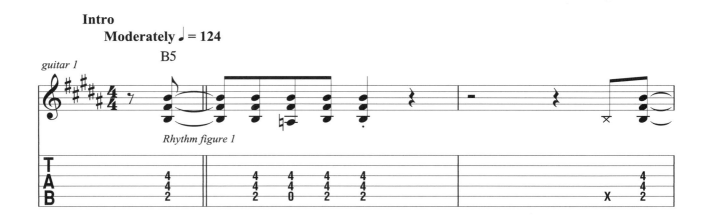

(spoken) I see trouble comin', man.

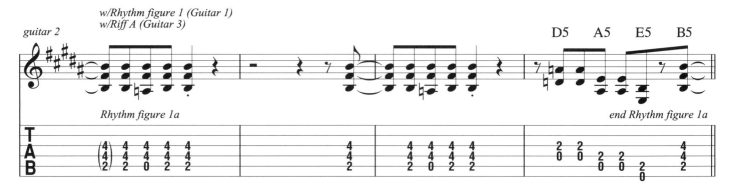

Verse

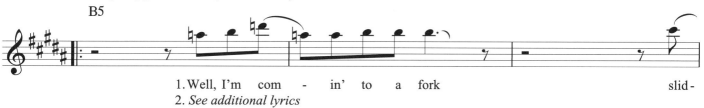

1. Well, I'm com - in' to a fork
2. *See additional lyrics*

in' down the road.

Gon - na lick 'em on ___ down,

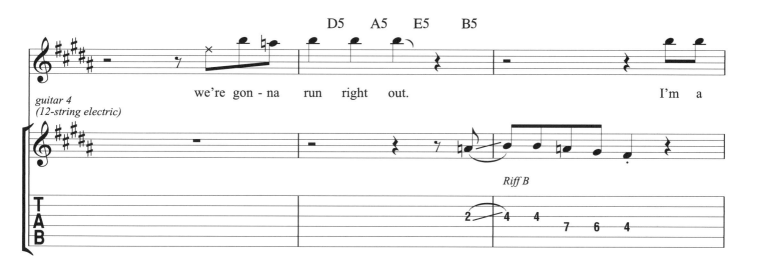

we're gon - na run right out.

I'm a

fight - in' fool, ____

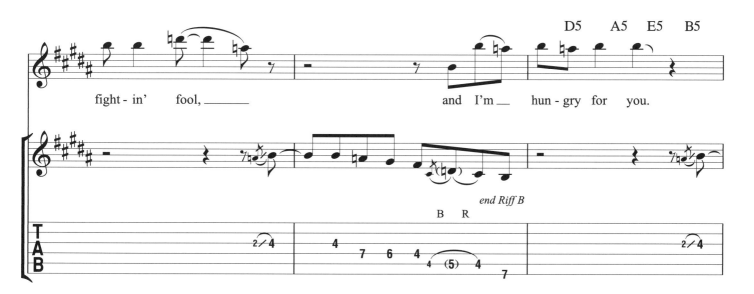

and I'm ___ hun - gry for you.

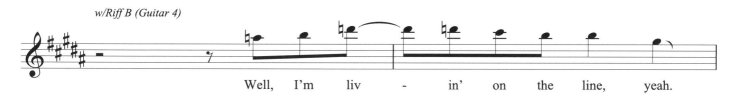

Well, I'm liv - in' on the line, yeah.

Chorus

Guitar Solo

Additional lyrics

2nd Verse:
Make your heartbeat thump
Make your starter jump, yeah
You're runnin' all the time, yeah
And then you're fightin' all night
With my rockin' shoes
'Cause I'm hungry for you
Well, I'm livin' on the line, yeah
All my life

Wheels

Words & Music by Angus Young & Malcolm Young

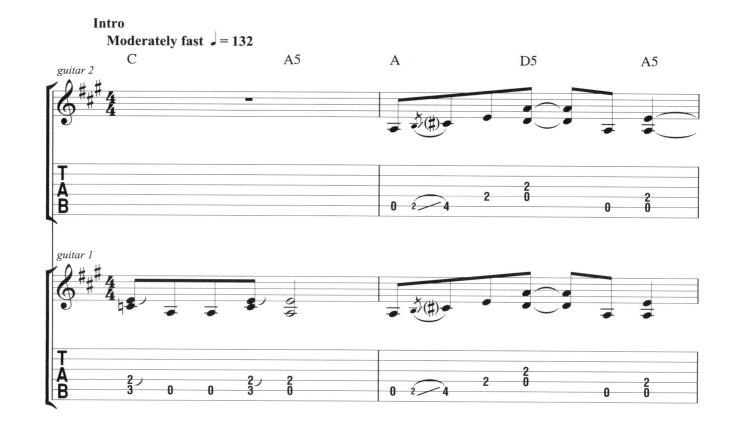

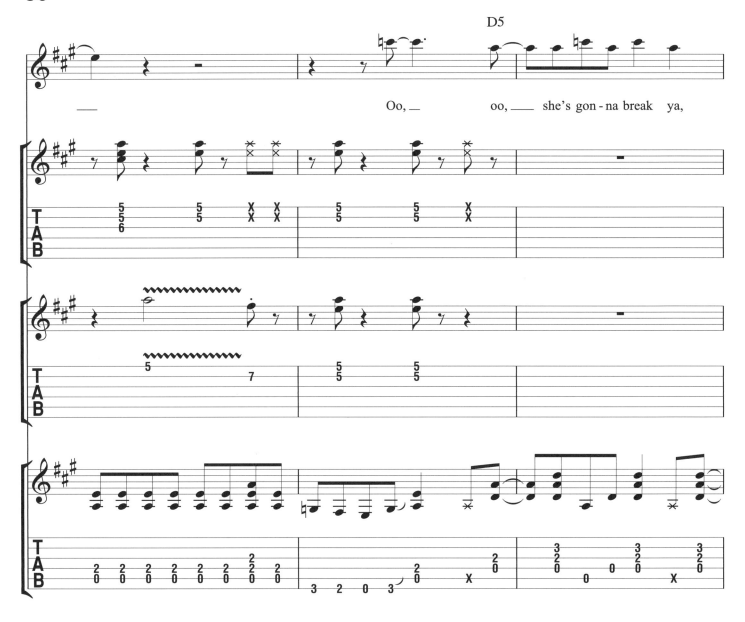

Oo, __ oo, __ she's gon - na break ya,

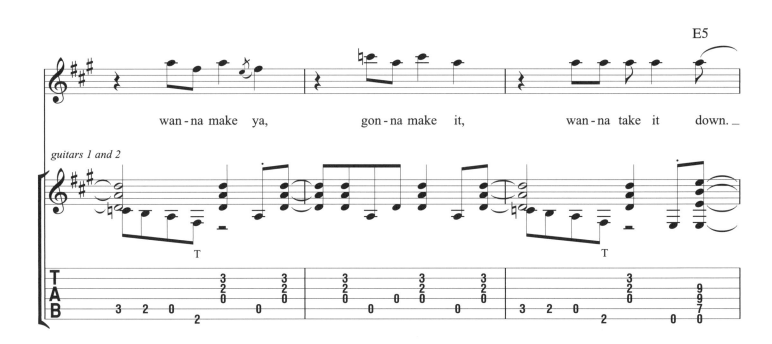

wan - na make ya, gon - na make it, wan - na take it down. __

She gon - na

rock 'n' roll 'n slide it down, _____ yeah! _____

Chorus

Wheels   spin - nin' a - round _ my   brain, _   an'

Rhythm figure 1

*Composite arrangement

go - in' through __ the red.

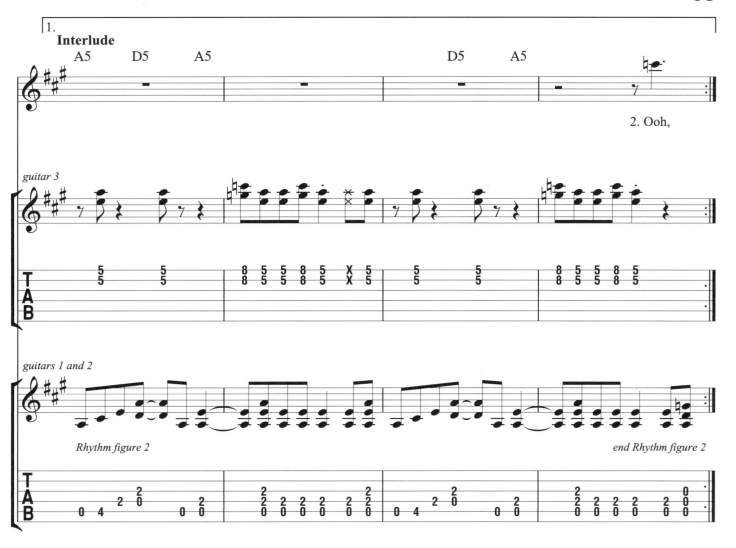

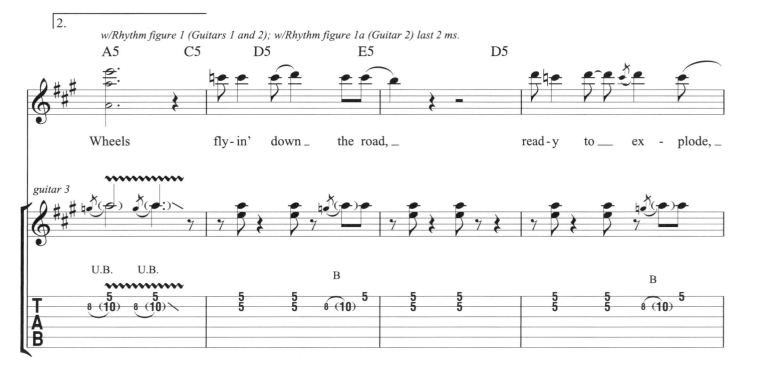

96

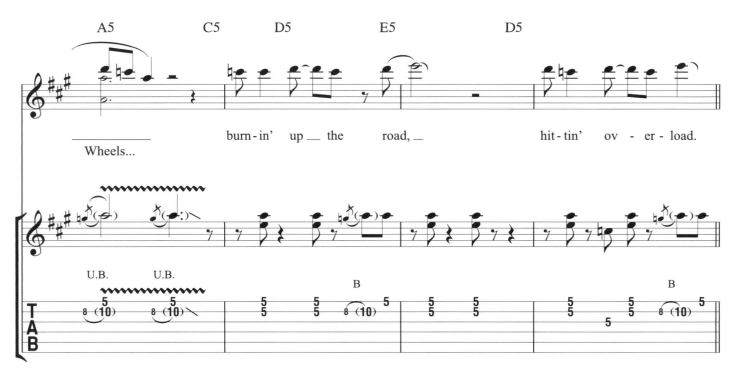

burn-in' up ___ the road, ___ hit-tin' ov-er-load.

Wheels...

Interlude

w/Rhythm figure 2 (Guitars 1 and 2)

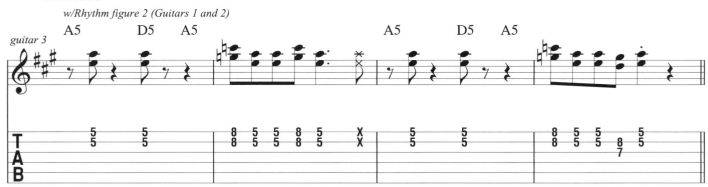

Guitar Solo

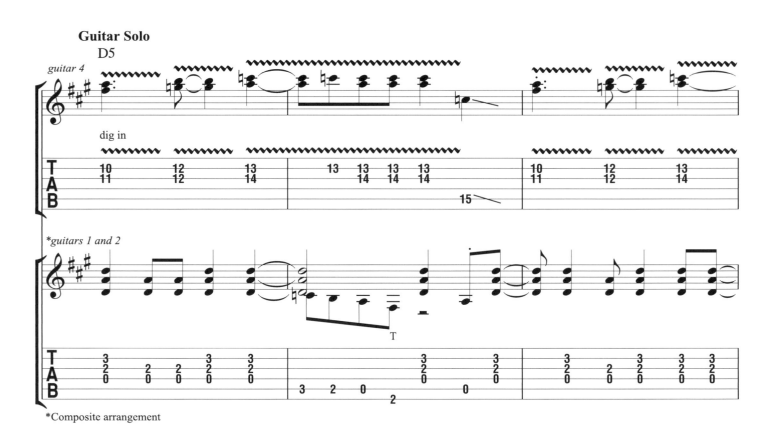

*Composite arrangement

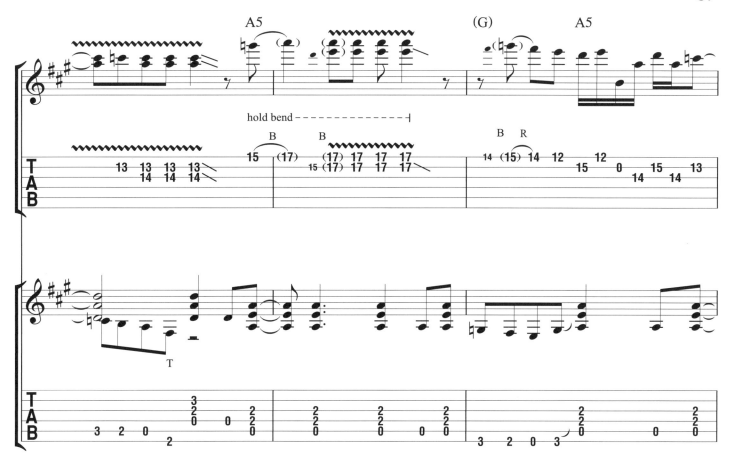

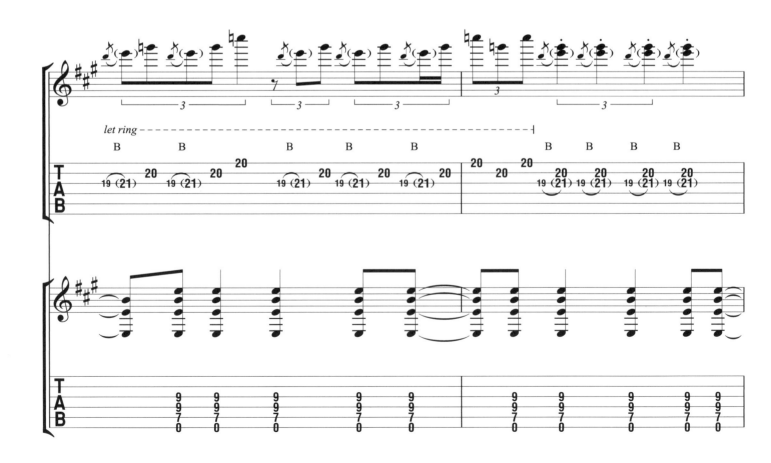

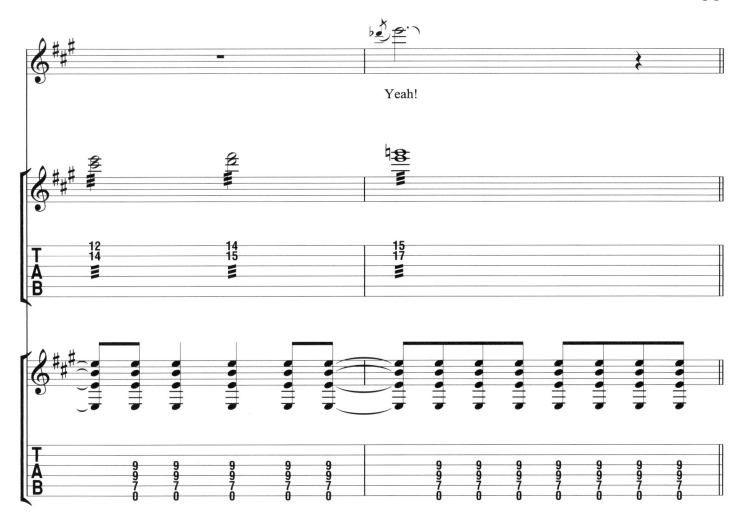

Yeah!

Chorus

w/Rhythm figure 1 (Guitars 1 and 2) 2 times; w/Rhythm figure 1a (Guitar 2) on last 2 ms.

A5   C5   D5   E5   D5

Wheels spin-nin' a-round my brain,   an'

guitar 3

U.B.

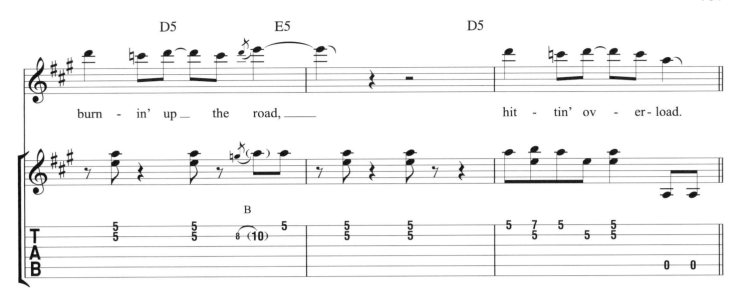

burn - in' up_ the road, _____ hit - tin' ov - er - load.

Outro Chorus

w/Rhythm figure 2 (Guitars 1 and 2) 4 times

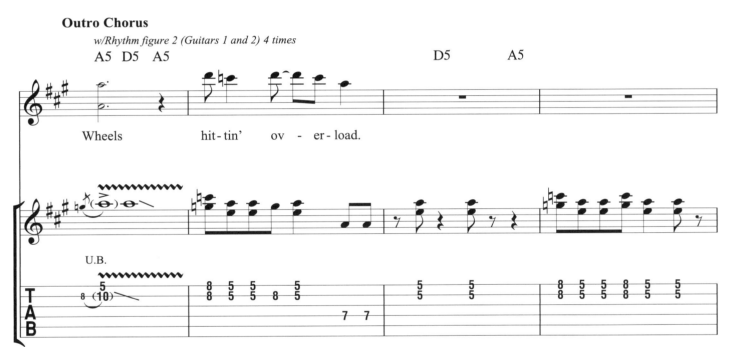

Wheels hit - tin' ov - er - load.

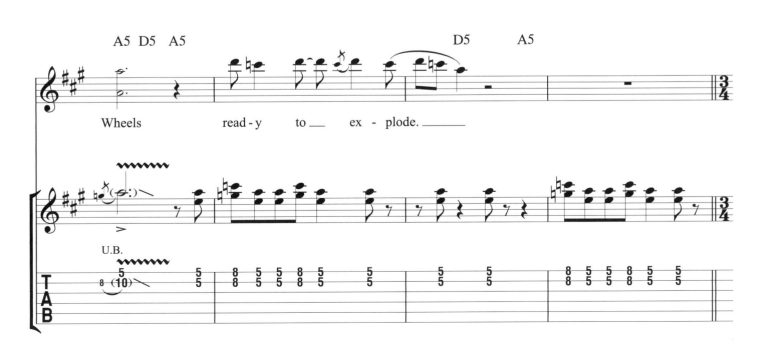

Wheels read - y to __ ex - plode. _____

Outro

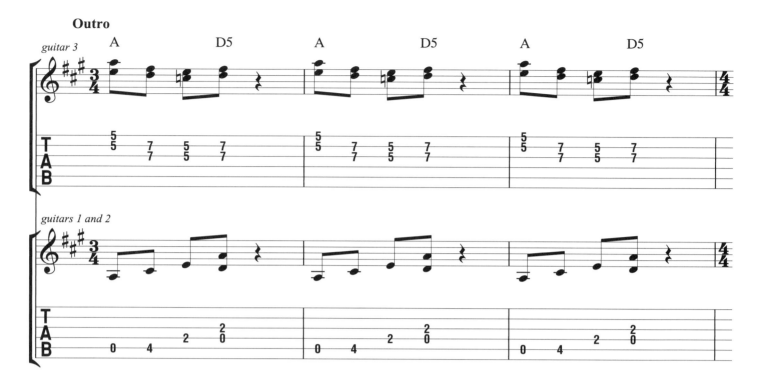

Freely

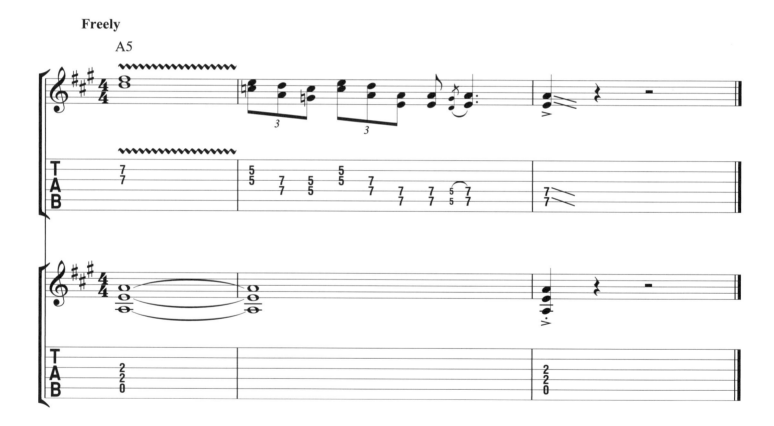

Additional lyrics

2nd Verse:
Ooh, she wanna shake you, no way to save you
She got me shocked, I'm fallin'
I'm blowin' it out
Know what I'm talkin' about
Ooh, she gonna ride you, wanna slide you
Ain't no fakin', she wanna take you out
You betcha right, she gonna spin you 'round, yeah

Decibel

Words & Music by Angus Young & Malcolm Young

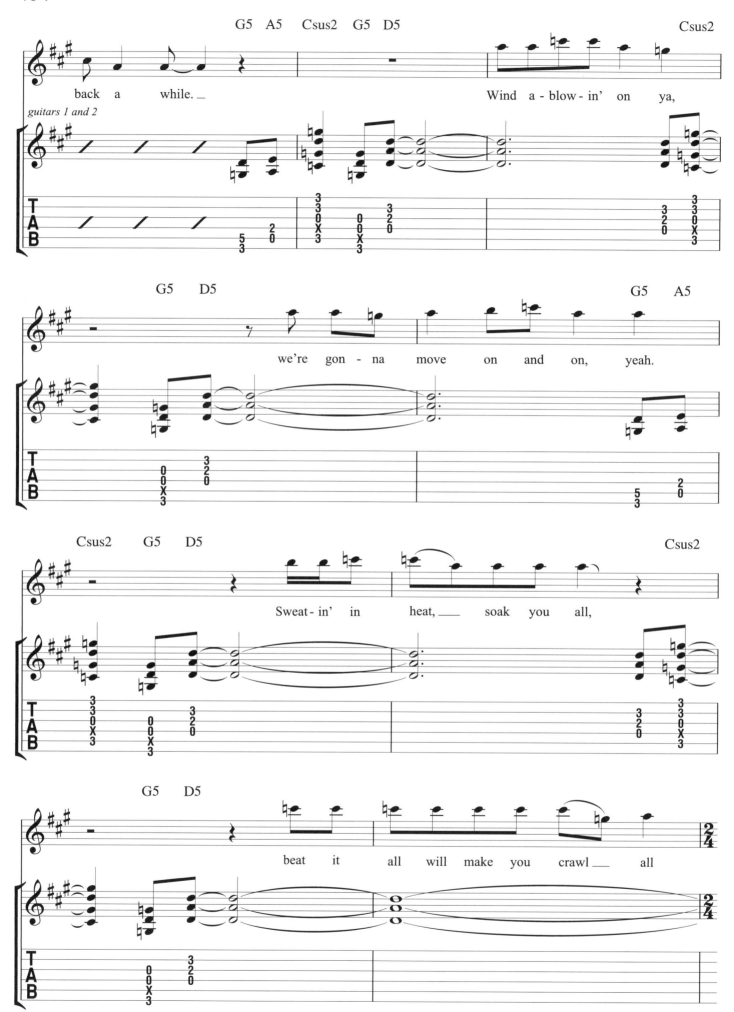

Chorus
(A)

night, de - ci - bel.

Aw, _____ de - ci - bel.

Verse
(A)

Has you from deep in - side, _

you were wav - in', then you

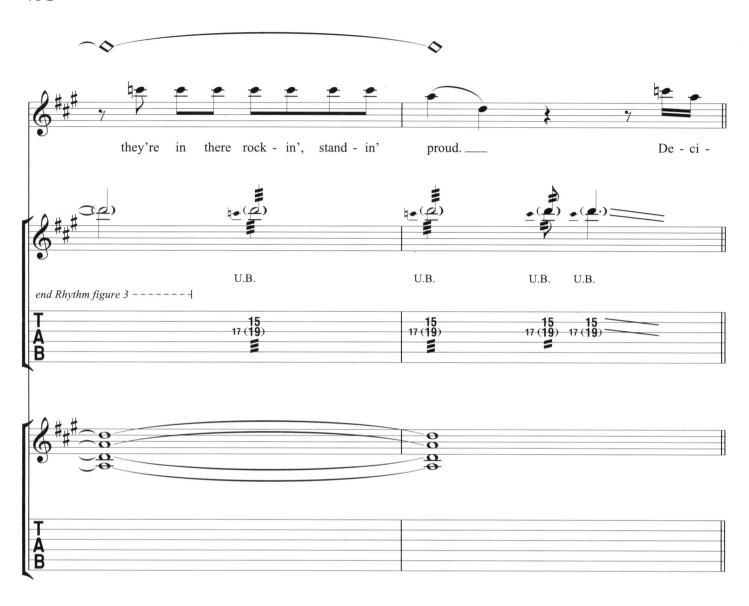

they're in there rock - in', stand - in' proud. ____ De - ci -

U.B.   U.B.   U.B.   U.B.

end Rhythm figure 3 - - - - - - -|

Chorus

(A)

bel.   That's the his - tor - y of rock 'n' roll, ____ de - ci - bel,

guitars 1 and 2

P.M. - - - - - - - - - - - - - - - -| P.M. -|

Guitar Solo

(A)

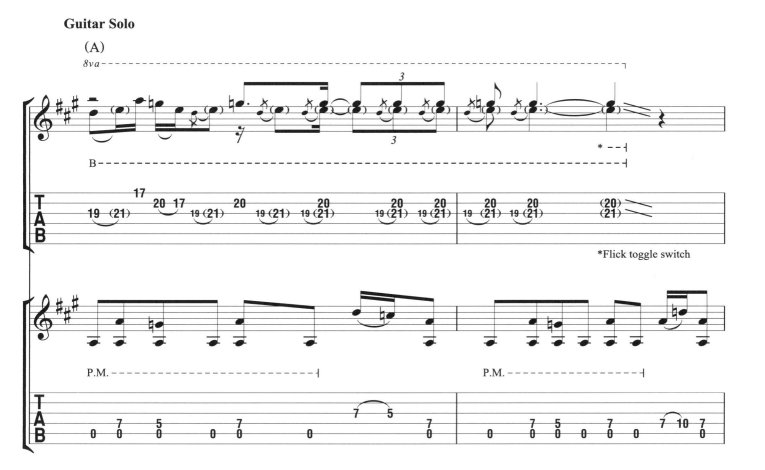

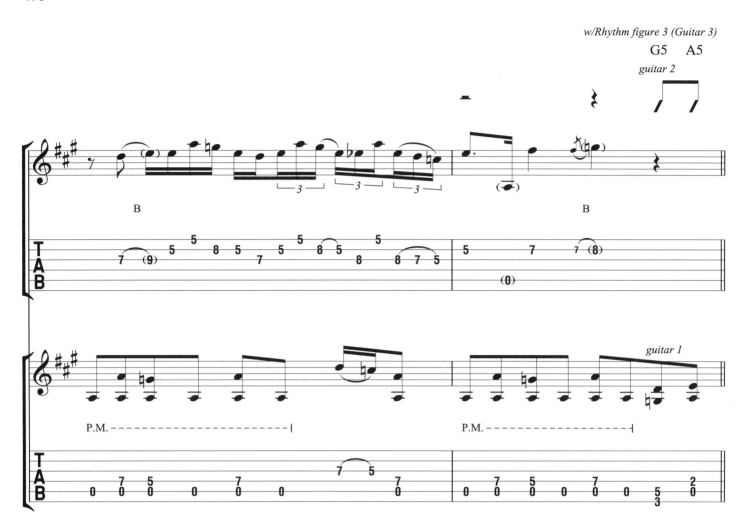

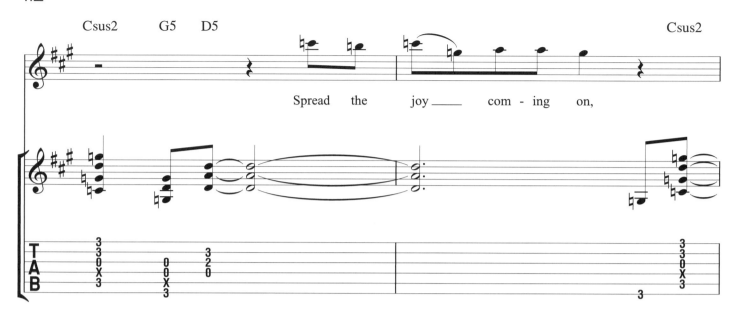

Spread the joy___ com - ing on,

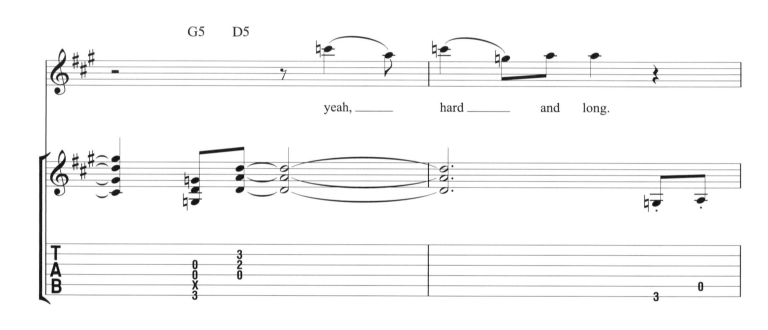

yeah, ___ hard ___ and long.

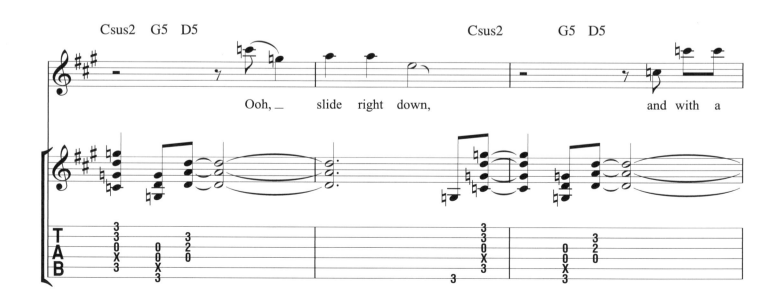

Ooh, __ slide right down, and with a

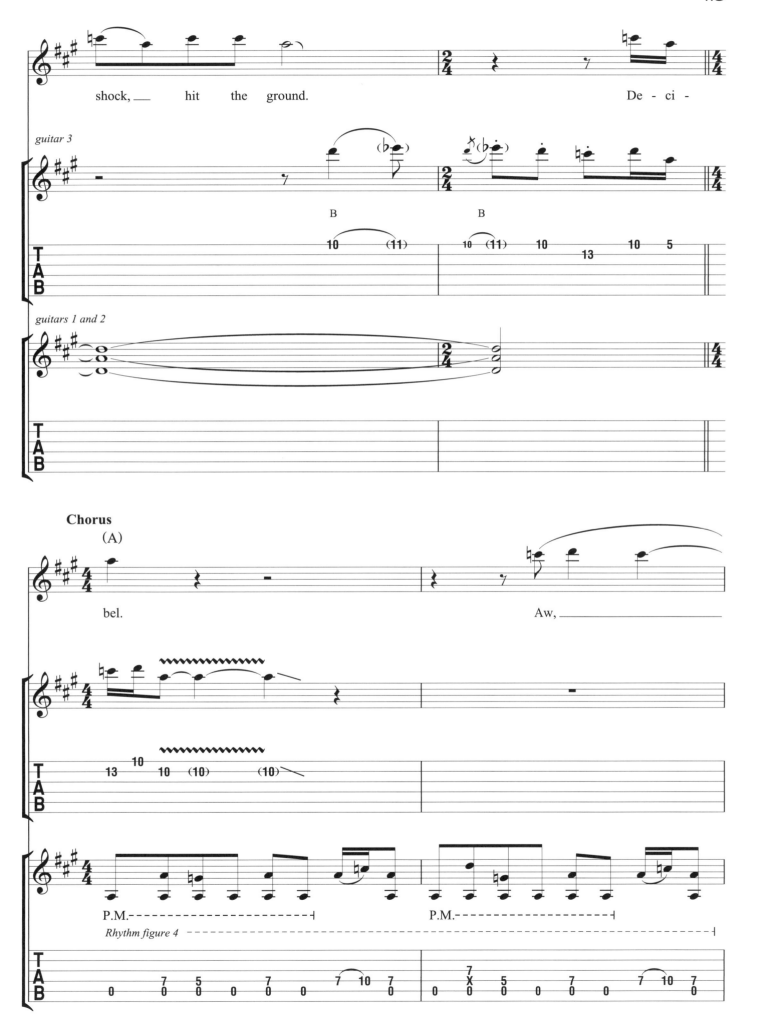

w/Rhythm figure 4 (Guitars 1 and 2) 4 1/2 times

___ de - ci - bel.

Ooh, _____ de-ci-

guitar 3

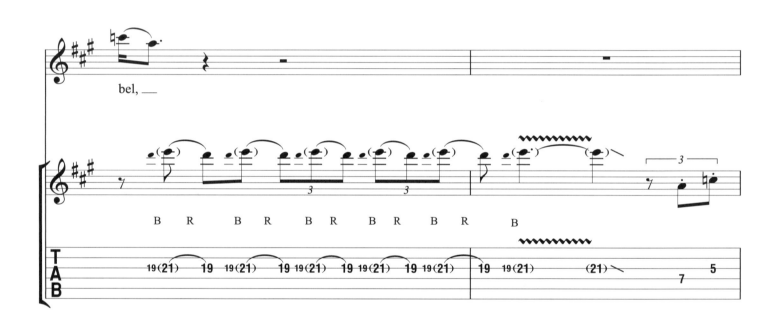

bel, ___

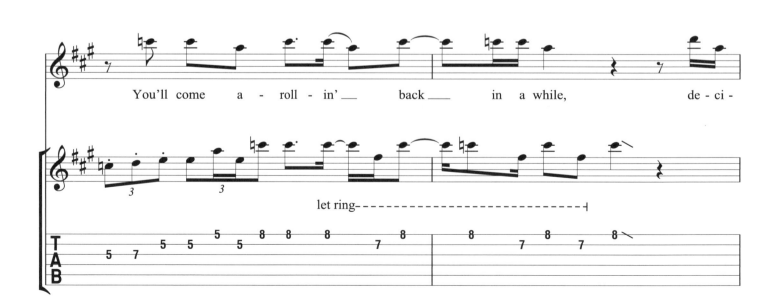

You'll come a - roll - in' ___ back ___ in a while, ___ de-ci-

let ring

bel.   Ooh, _____ yeah, _   de - ci -

w/Rhythm figure 3 (Guitar 3)

guitar 2

G5 A5

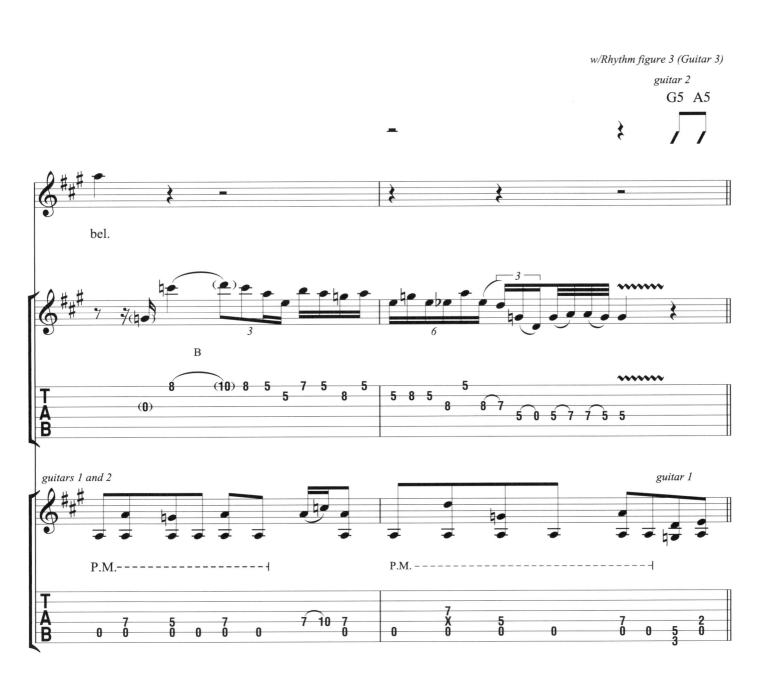

bel.

guitars 1 and 2   guitar 1

de - ci -

Outro

She Likes Rock N Roll
Words & Music by Angus Young & Malcolm Young

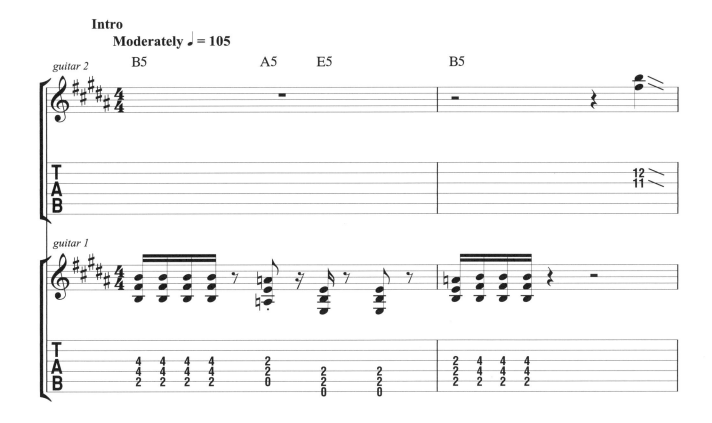

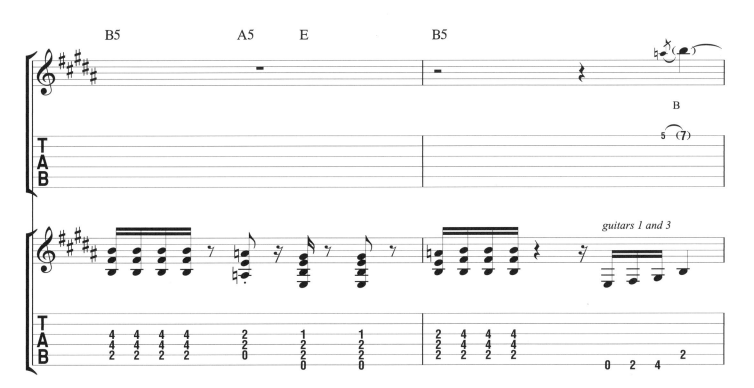

Guitar Solo

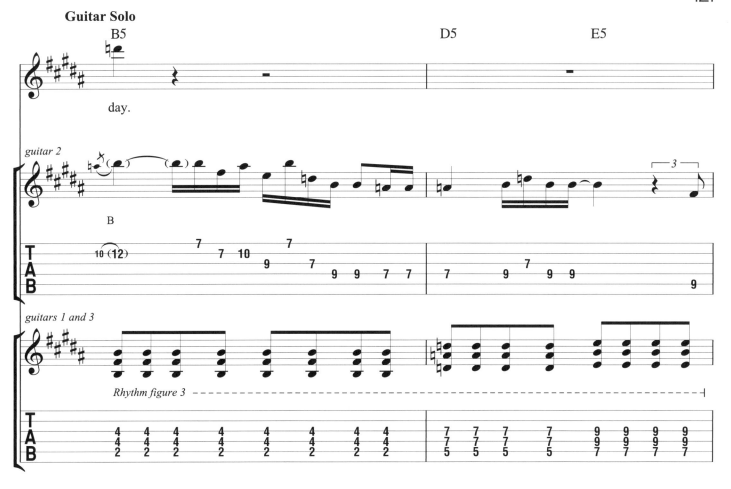

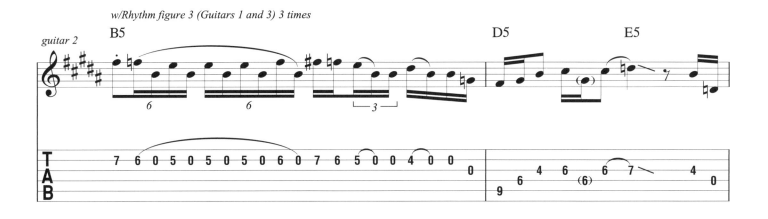

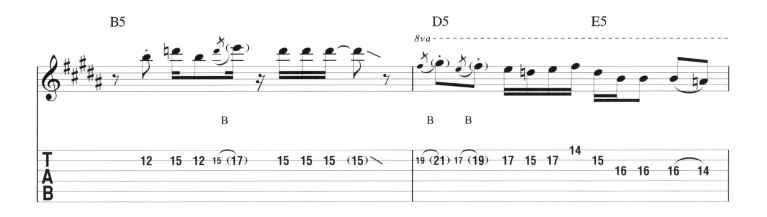

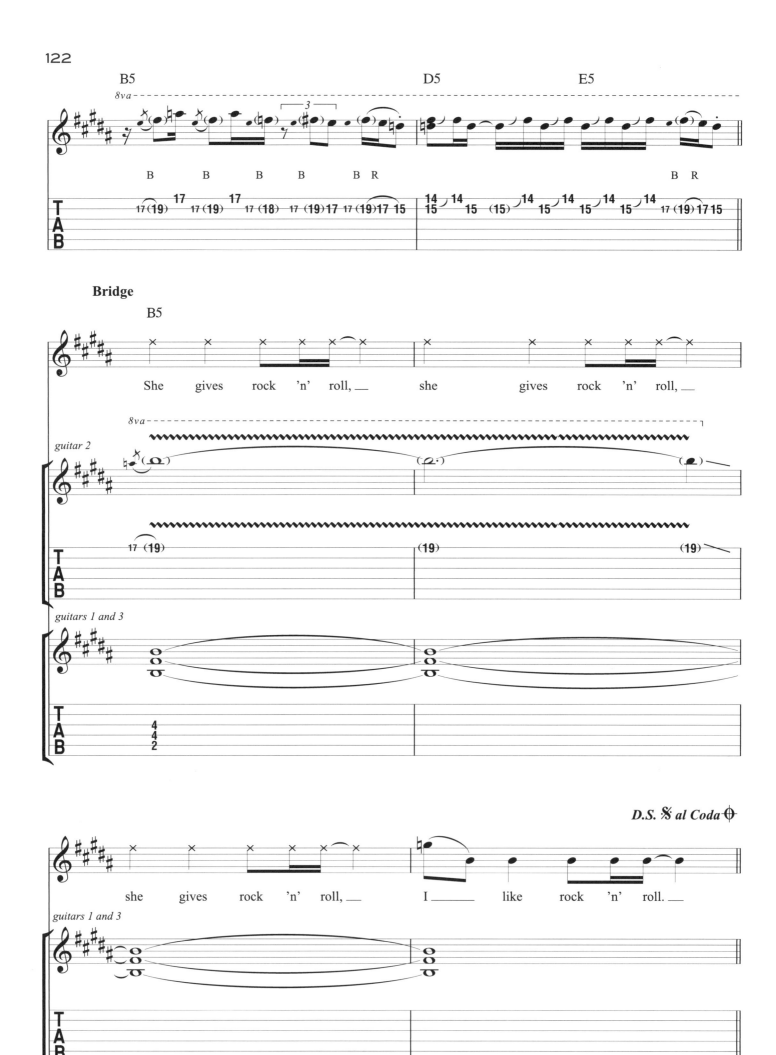

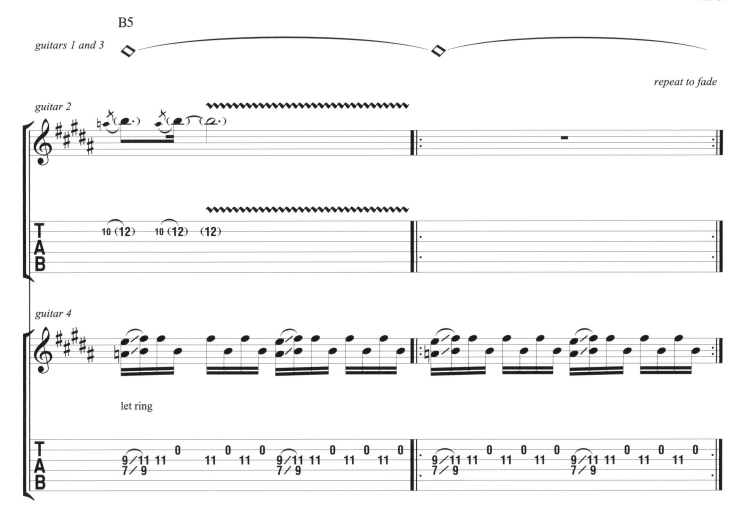

Additional lyrics

2nd Verse:
You're gonna rock, you'll rock the night away
You're gonna roll, baby, and I'll make the grade
We're gonna rock now, rock 'n' rollin' all in the town
You're gonna make it right, we're gonna need rock all night

3rd Verse:
We're a hurricane comin' down
We're gonna rock all night, rock 'n' rollin' all the time
She may be home, rollin' out the groove
You know that rock 'n' roll's squeezin' out the tube

4th Verse:
I'm gonna dance all night long
And rock into the room, yeah
She likes sugar and I like honey, too
We're gonna rock it, I ain't gonna mess around with you

Stormy May Day

Words & Music by Angus Young & Malcolm Young

Intro
Freely

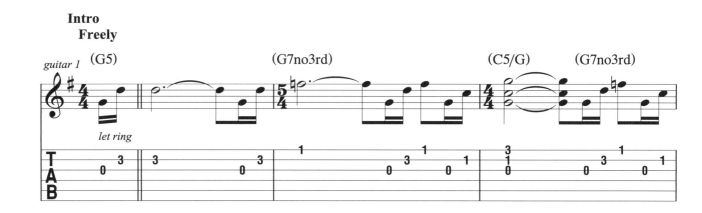

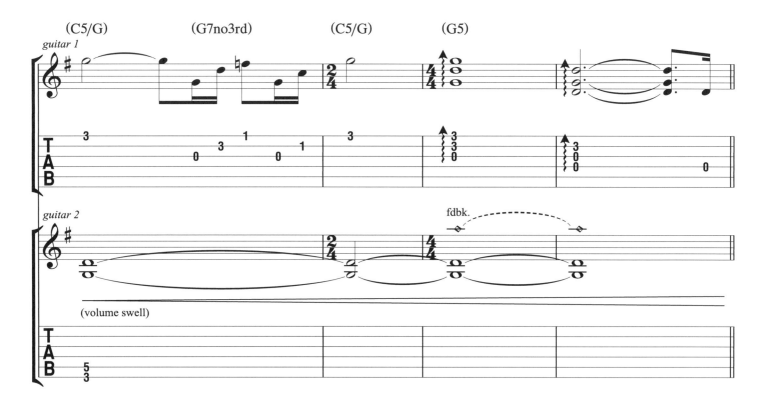

Moderately ♩ = 95

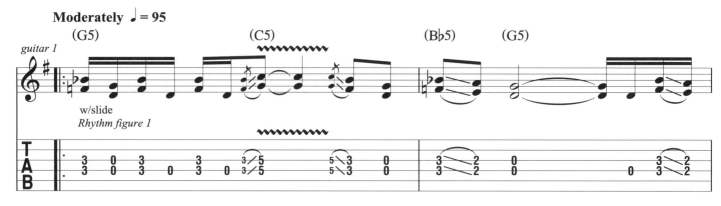

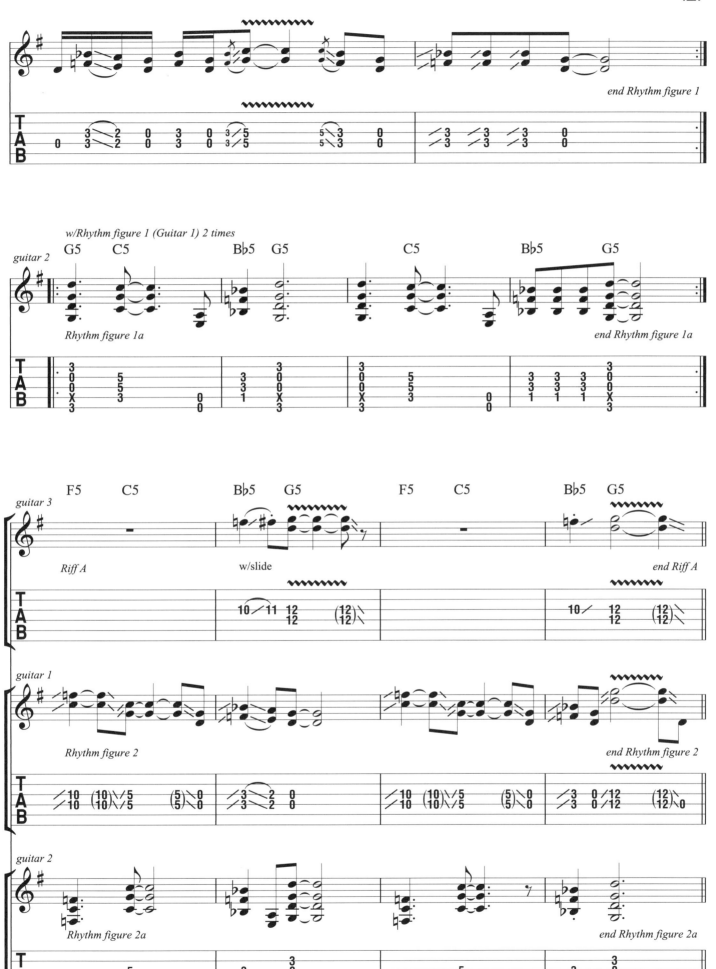

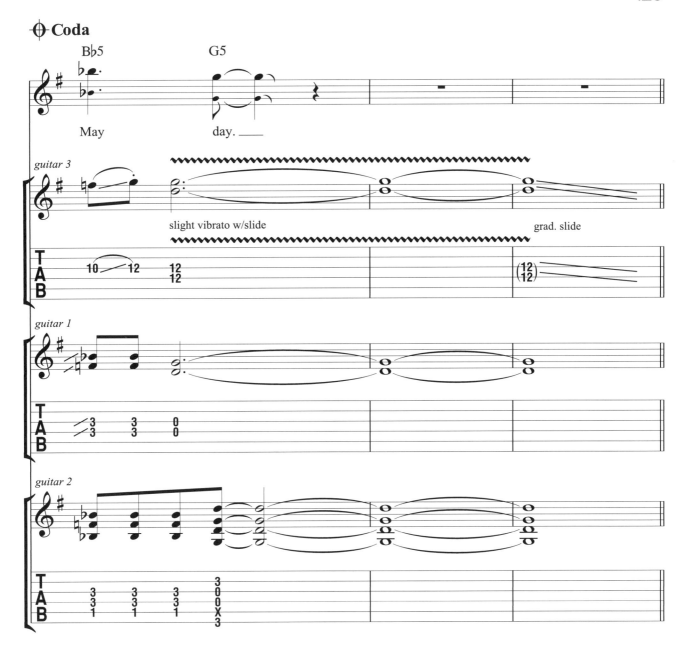

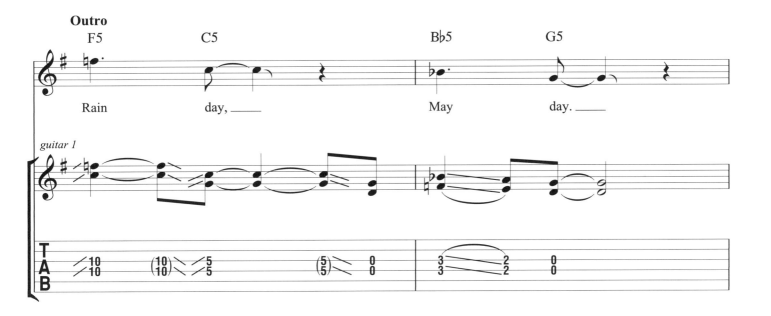

Additional lyrics

2nd Verse:
The sky is dark'nin', the dogs are barkin'
A call for help, you hope they get you through
A clap of thunder, a split asunder
The people runnin' and the moon don't rise

Money Made

Words & Music by Angus Young & Malcolm Young

Chorus

w/Rhythm figures 2 and 2a (Guitars 2 and 3) 4 times

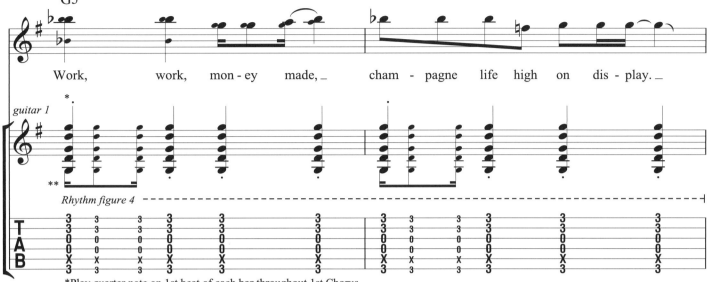

Work, work, mon-ey made, _ cham-pagne life high on dis-play. _

guitar 1

Rhythm figure 4

*Play quarter note on 1st beat of each bar throughout 1st Chorus.
**Play indicated rhythm on 1st beat of each bar throughout 2nd Chorus.

w/Rhythm figure 4 (Guitar 1) 3 times

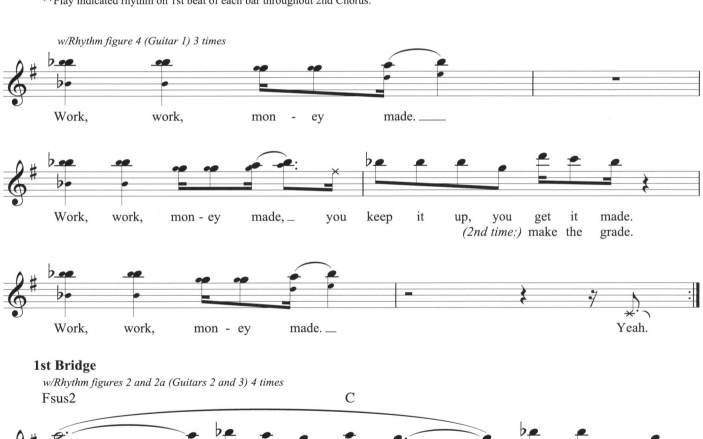

Work, work, mon-ey made. _____

Work, work, mon-ey made, _ you keep it up, you get it made.
(2nd time:) make the grade.

Work, work, mon-ey made. _ Yeah.

1st Bridge

w/Rhythm figures 2 and 2a (Guitars 2 and 3) 4 times

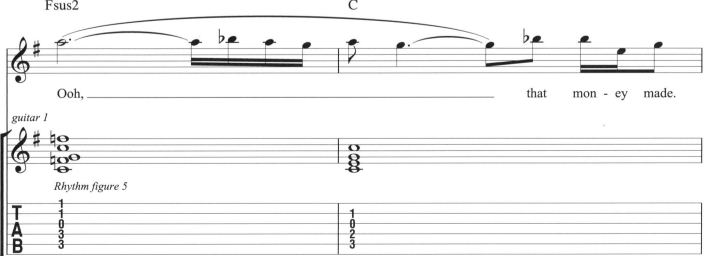

Ooh, _____ that mon-ey made.

guitar 1

Rhythm figure 5

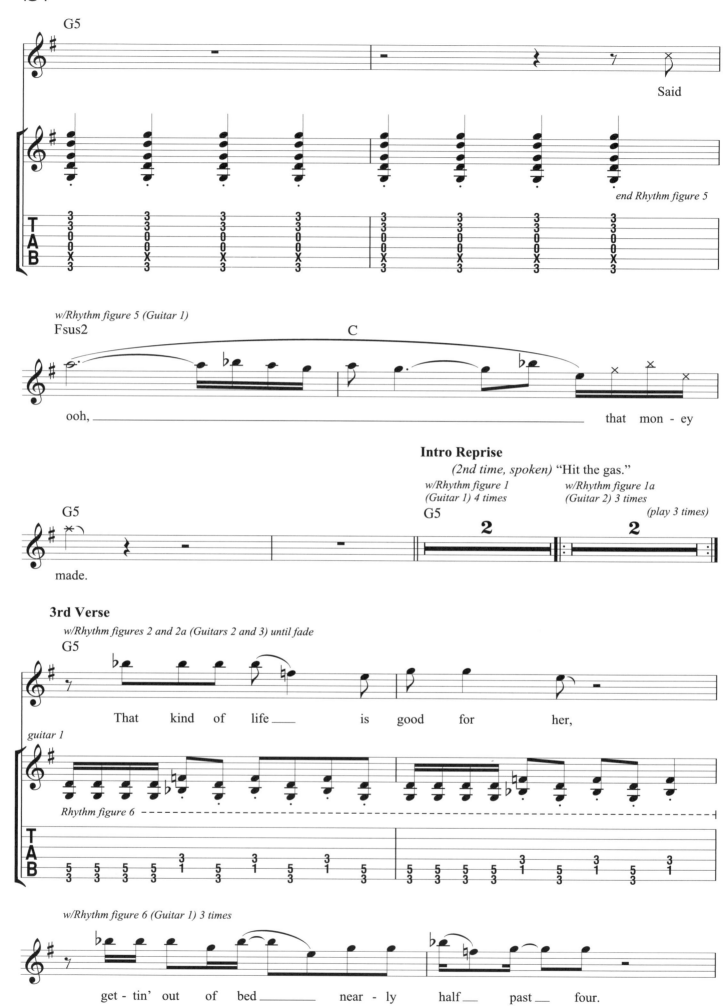

Additional lyrics

2nd Verse:
Can't bring me into Hollywood
See you livin' it up, it feels mighty good
Recommendations all around
Come taste the sweet life, that's what it's all about
That money made

Rock N Roll Dream

Words & Music by Angus Young & Malcolm Young

*Gtrs. 1, 2, 4, 5 Capo I (or tune up 1/2 step)
Gtr. 3 in standard tuning

Intro
Moderately ♩ = 106

*Music sounds 1/2 step higher than written.

1.Deep __ wa-ter all a-round __ me, _____
2. *See additional lyrics*

*Implied tonality

(G)   (D)   E5

an' cir - cle sharks _   all a - bout _

Rhythm figure 1a   end Rhythm figure 1a

let ring - ⌐ let ring - - - - - - - - - ⌐
Rhythm figure 1   end Rhythm figure 1

**Bass implied tonality

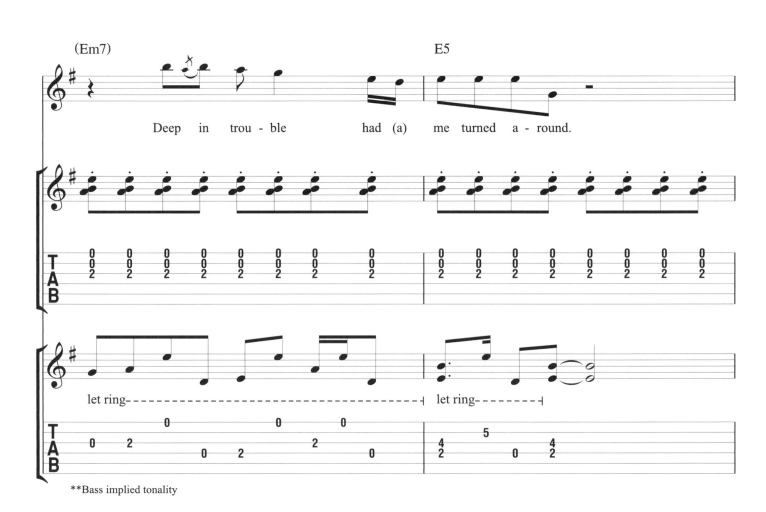

(Em7)   E5

Deep in trou - ble   had (a) me turned a - round.

let ring - ⌐ let ring - - - - - - - - ⌐

**Bass implied tonality

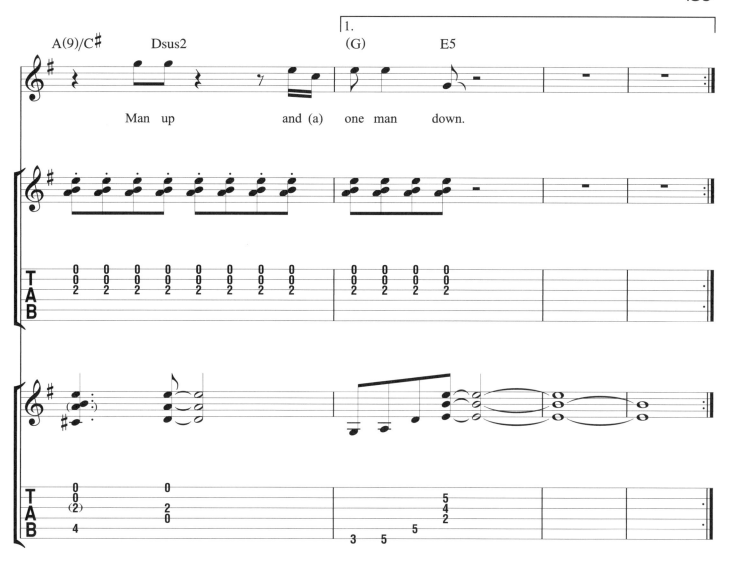

Man up and (a) one man down.

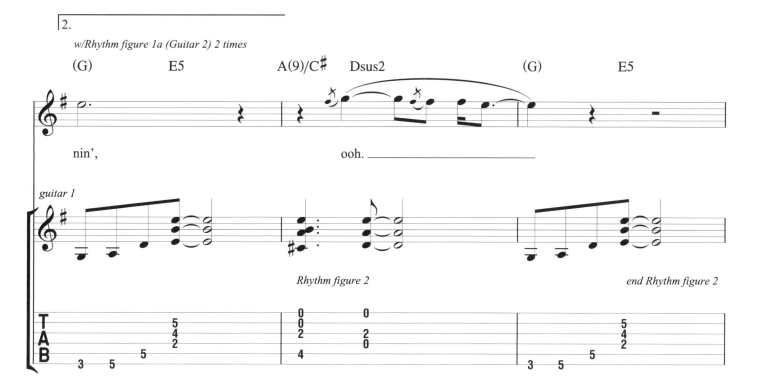

nin', ooh.

w/Rhythm figure 1a (Guitar 2) 2 times

guitar 1

Rhythm figure 2   *end Rhythm figure 2*

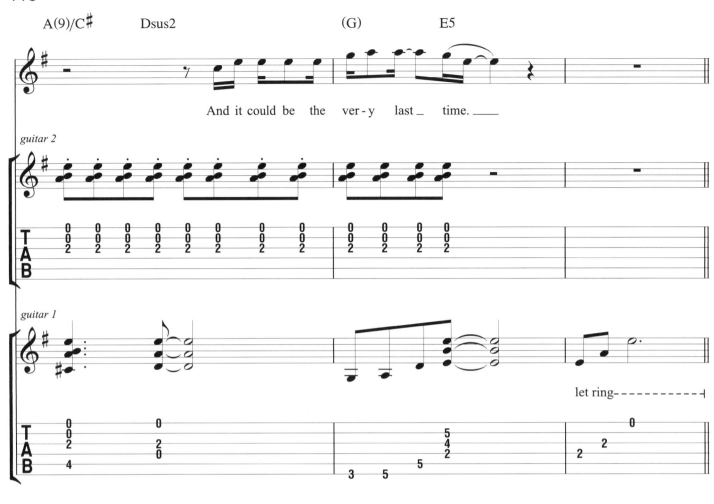

And it could be the ver-y last _ time. ____

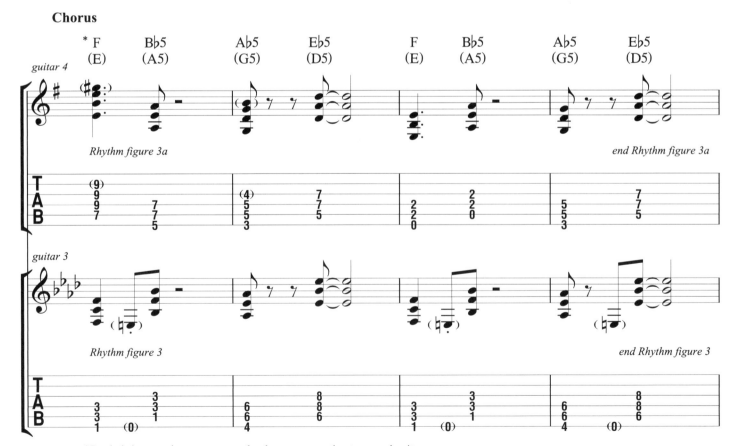

*Symbols in parentheses represent chord names respective to capoed guitar.
Symbols above reflect actual sounding chords.

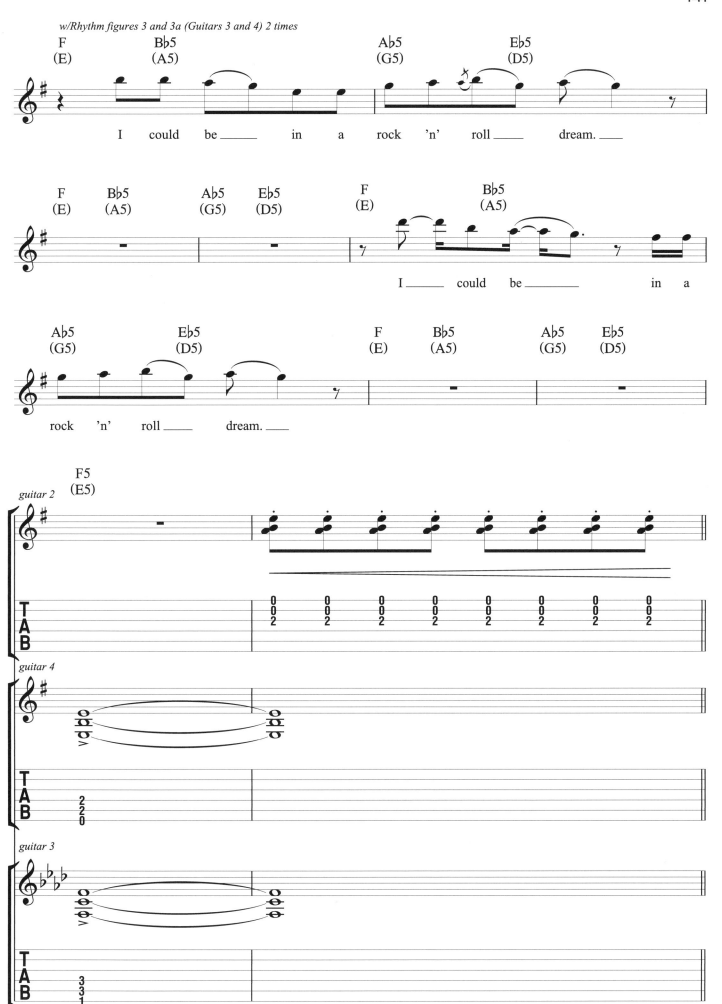

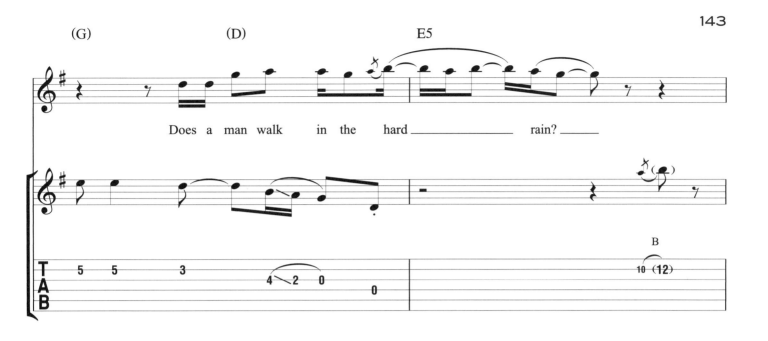

Does a man walk in the hard _____ rain? _____

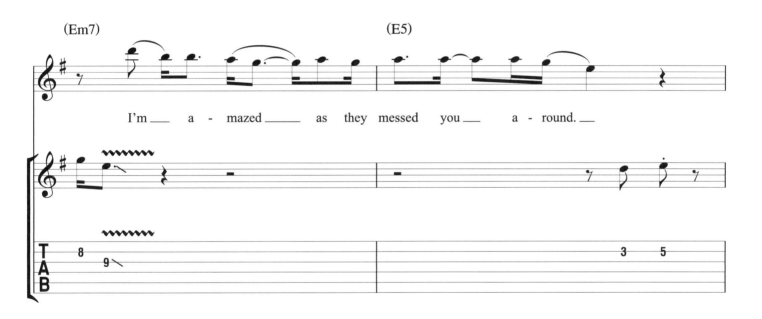

I'm ___ a - mazed _____ as they messed you ___ a - round. __

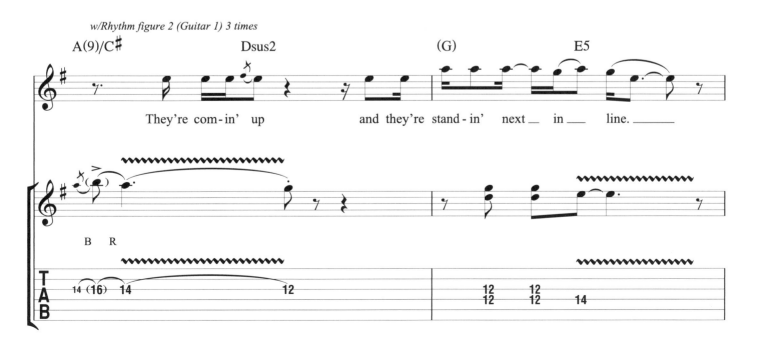

w/Rhythm figure 2 (Guitar 1) 3 times

They're com-in' up and they're stand-in' next __ in __ line. _____

% Chorus

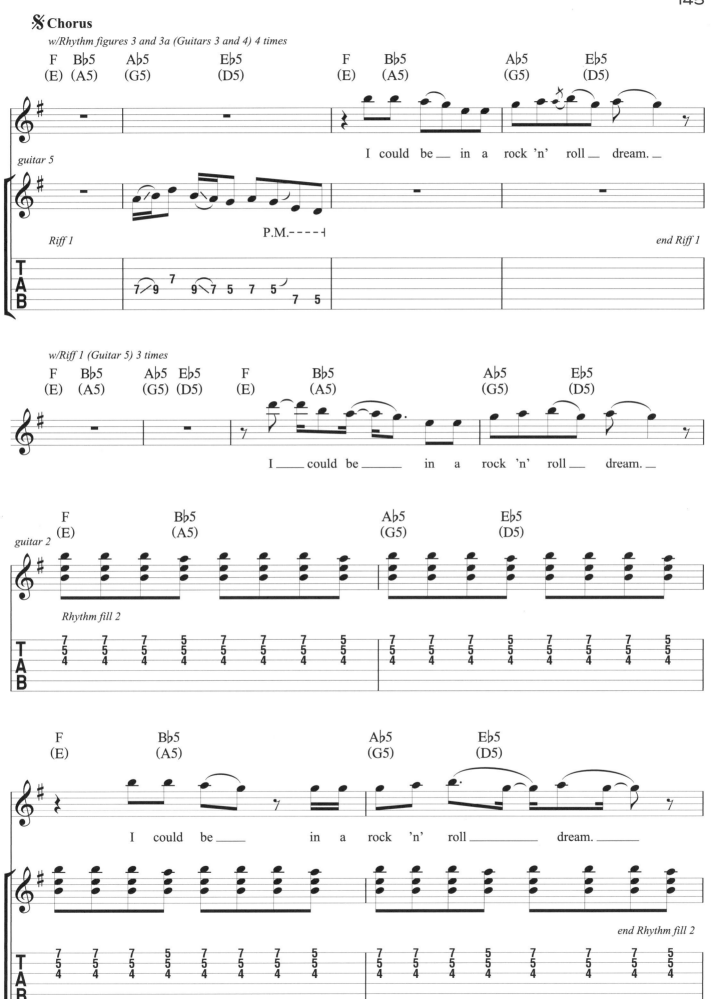

To Coda ⊕

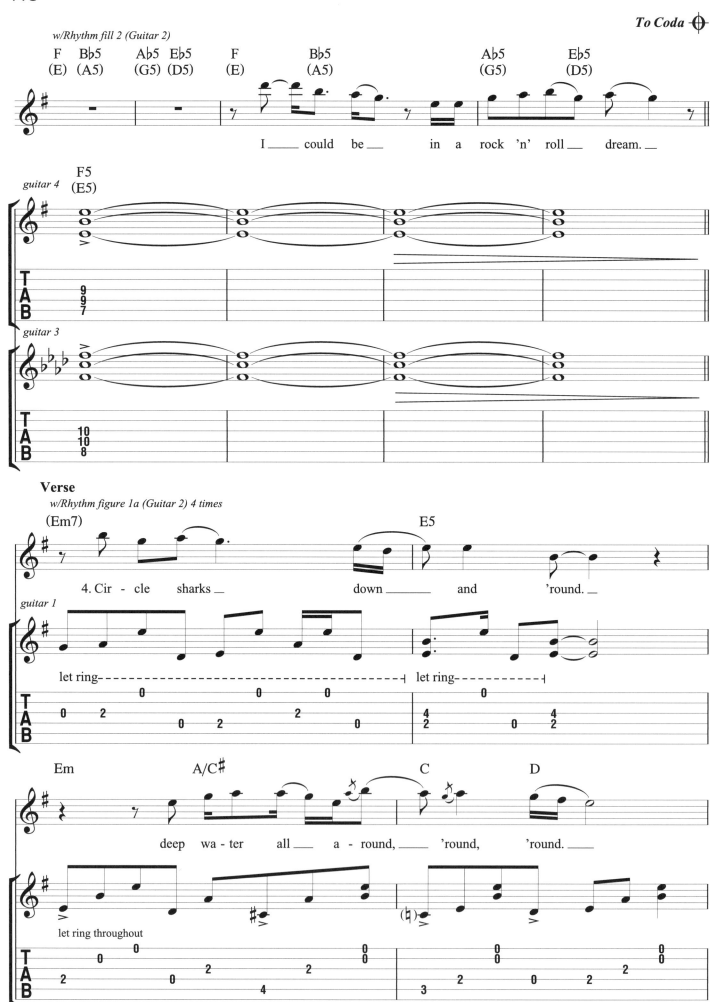

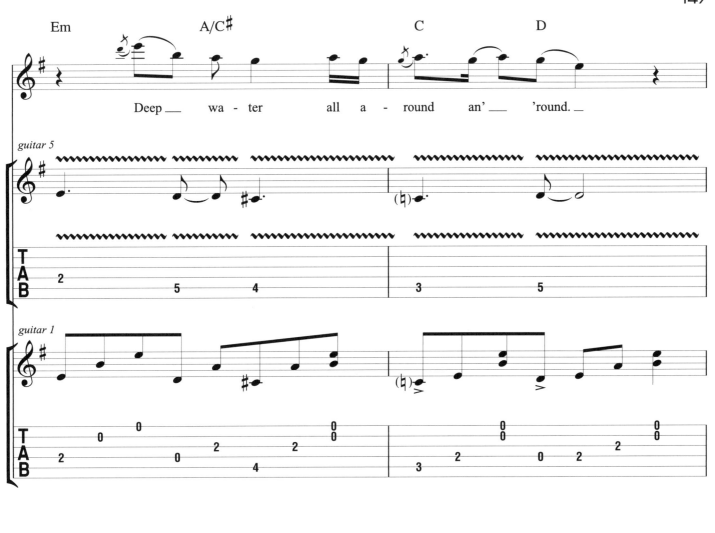

Deep __ wa - ter all a - round an' __ 'round. __

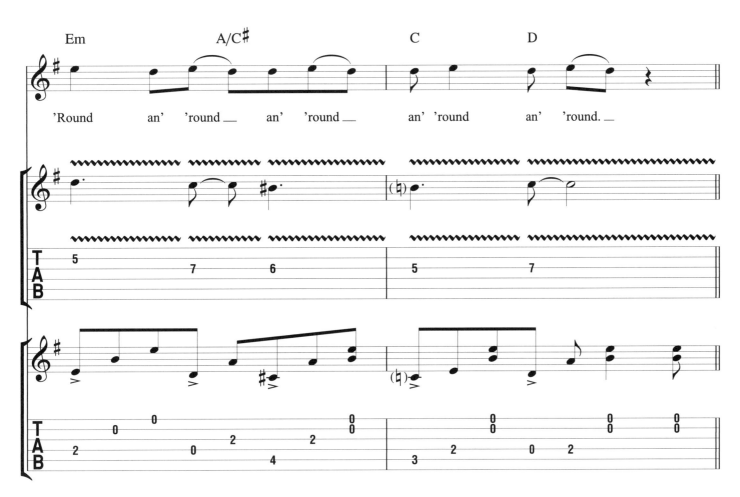

'Round an' 'round __ an' 'round __ an' 'round an' 'round. __

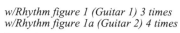

w/Rhythm figure 1 (Guitar 1) 3 times
w/Rhythm figure 1a (Guitar 2) 4 times

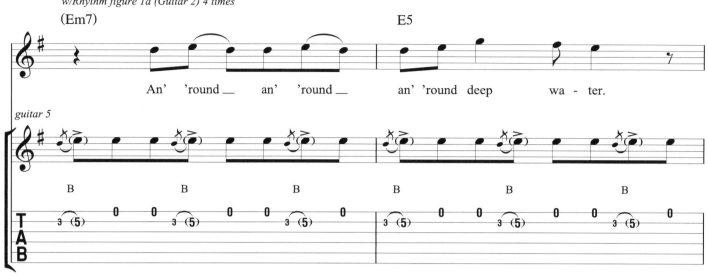

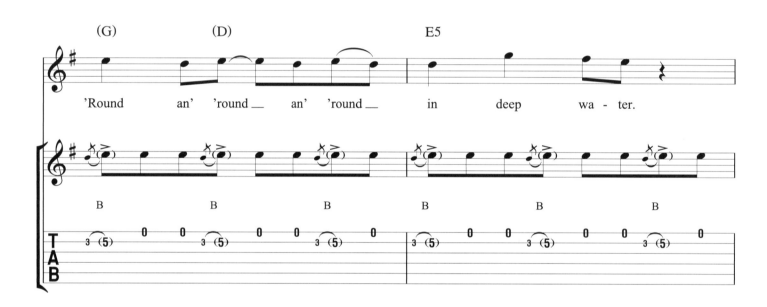

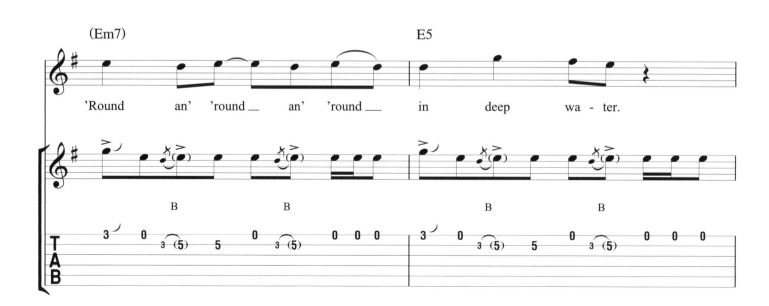

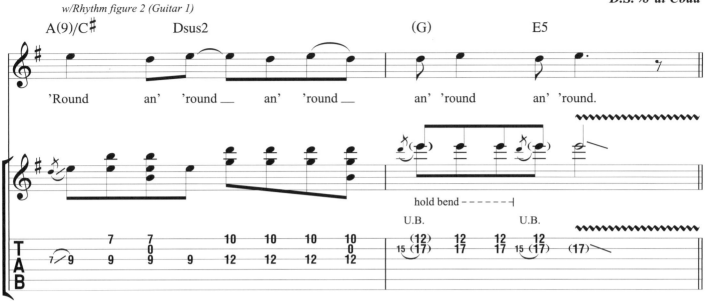

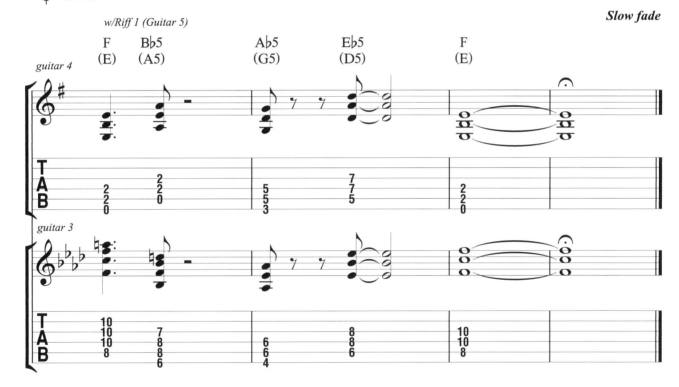

Additional lyrics

2nd Verse:
You pretty women gather 'round
You can't pick up not a single sound
You feel you're winnin'
That's what it's all about
Knowing you're winnin', ooh,
And it could be the very last time

Rocking All The Way
Words & Music by Angus Young & Malcolm Young

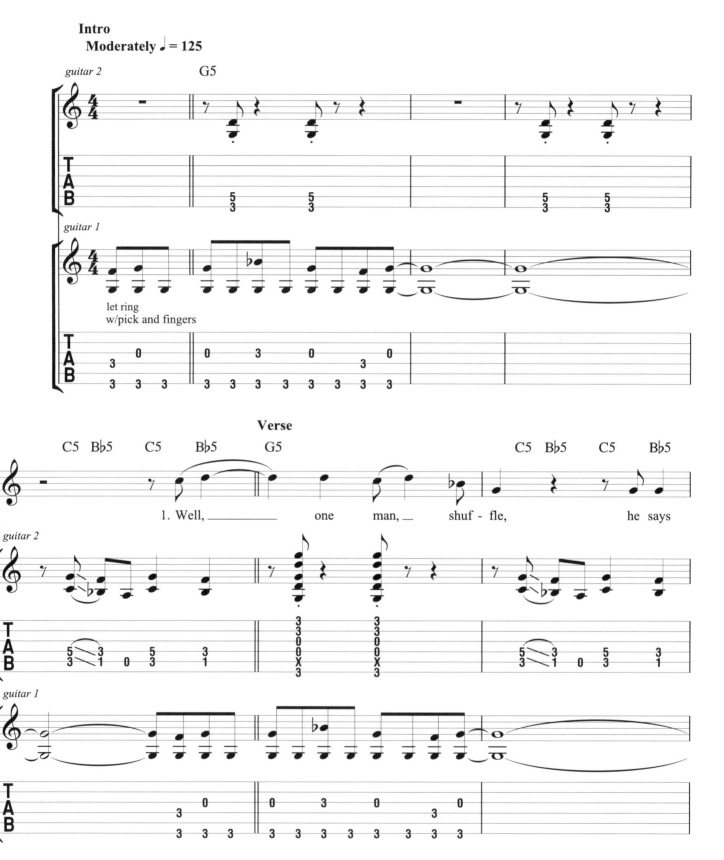

152

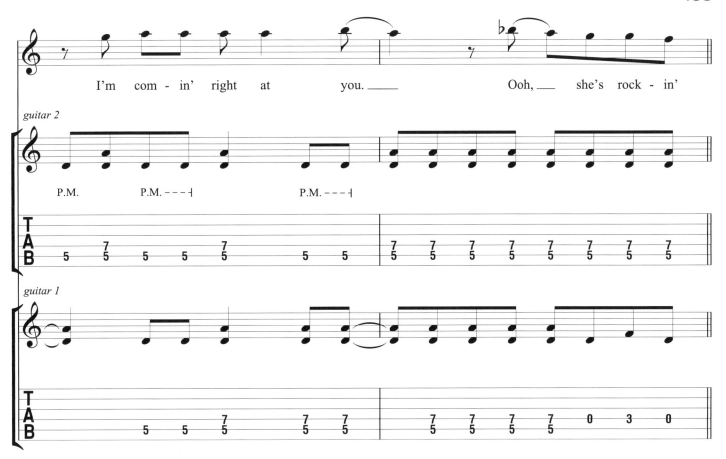

I'm com - in' right at you. _____ Ooh, _____ she's rock - in'

guitar 2

guitar 1

𝄌 **Chorus**

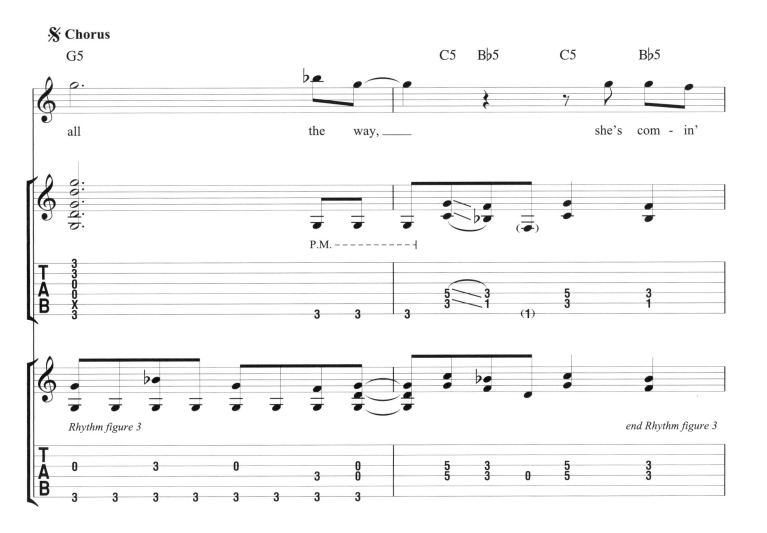

all   the way, _____   she's com - in'

Rhythm figure 3   *end Rhythm figure 3*

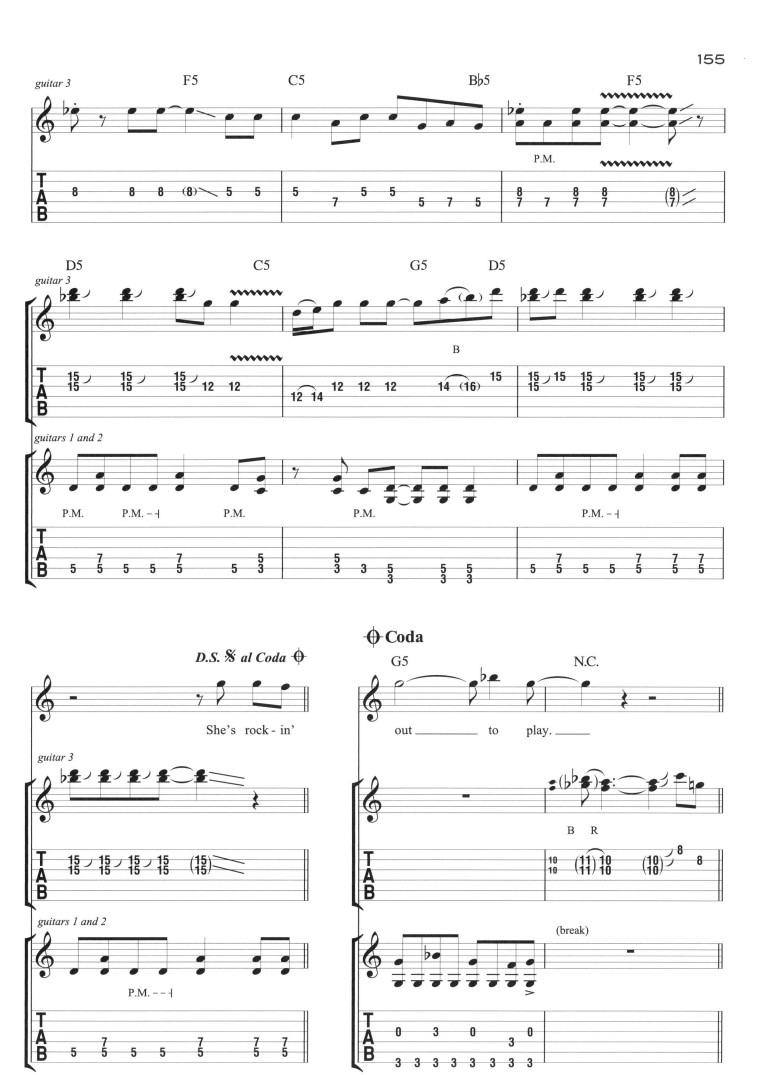

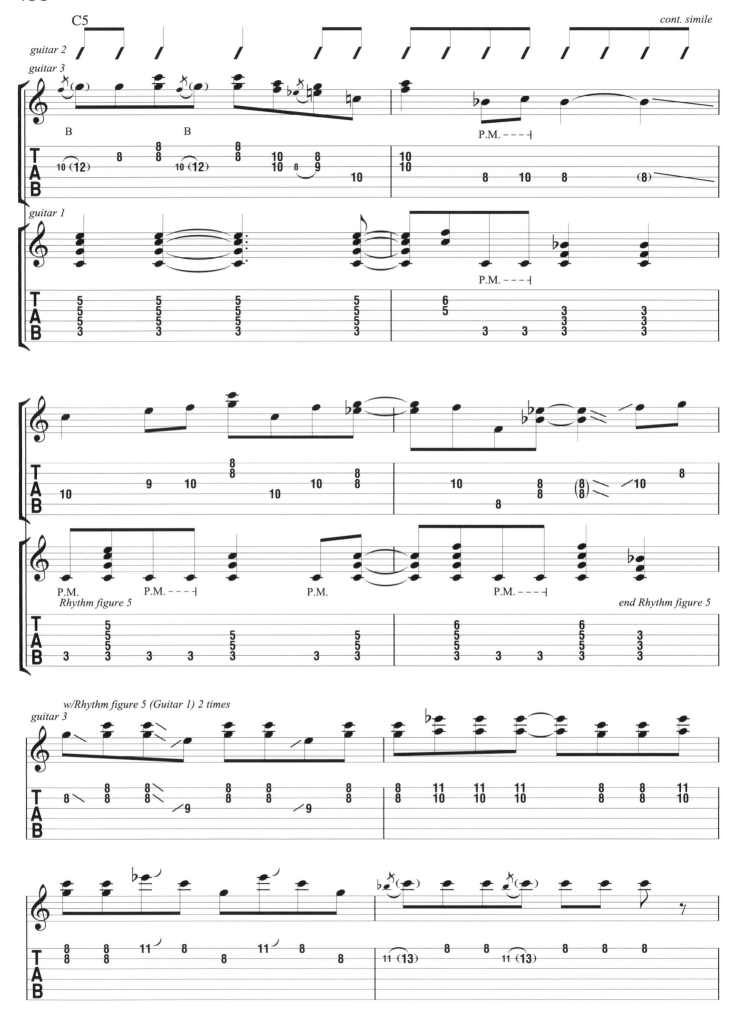

158

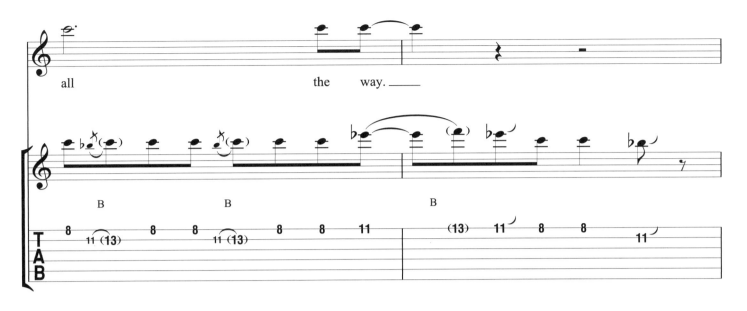

all   the   way. ___

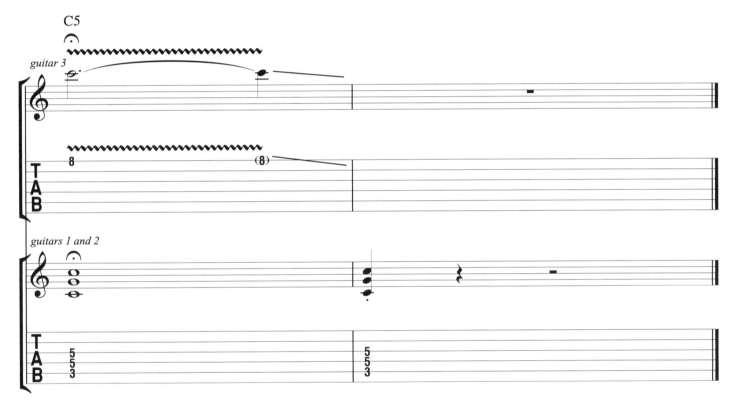

Additional lyrics

3rd Verse:
She's sexy in her boots, yeah
Tear up all the news
Shoot you in the back
Drivin' you mad
Come on, hear me out
And take my advice
She won't stop until you're in her sights

Black Ice
Words & Music by Angus Young & Malcolm Young

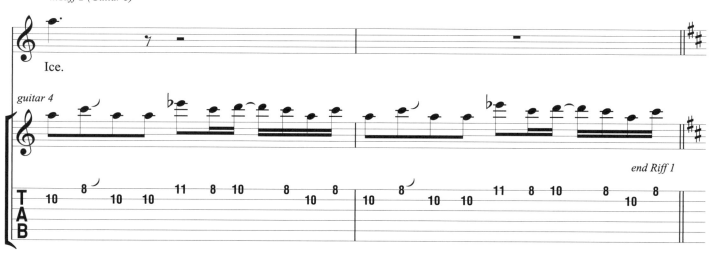

Verse

2. Come on and bleed - ing out ___ the crowds. ___

w/Riff 3 (Guitar 3) 3 times

we're watch - in' all ___ the wom - en go. ___

w/Rhythm figure 3 (Guitars 1 and 2)

Bm7

Man - y a mile ___ I'll nev - er take. ___

I run for for - ty miles ___ and I come up run - nin' late. ___

w/Rhythm figures 1 and 1a (Guitars 1 and 2)
w/Riff 2 (Guitar 3) 2 times
w/Riff 1 (Guitar 4)

Am7

Don't you know ___ I live it down, ___

when the dev - il come a - call - in' I ain't gon - na be a - round. ___

Chorus

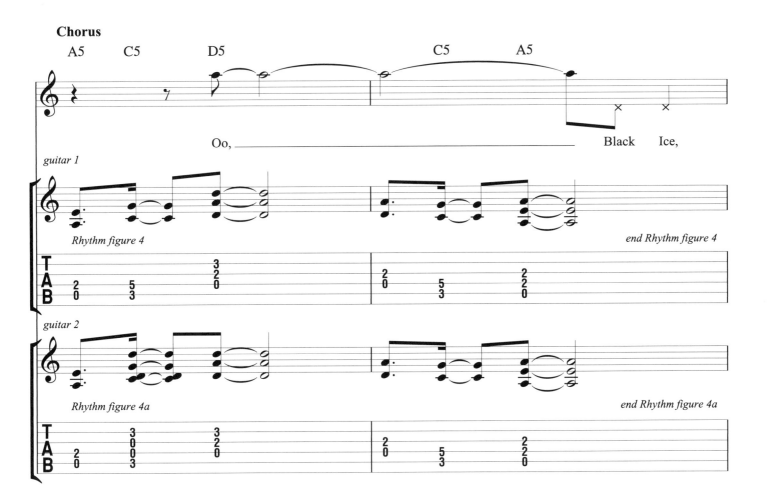

A5   C5   D5   C5   A5

Oo, _____ Black Ice,

guitar 1

Rhythm figure 4   *end Rhythm figure 4*

guitar 2

Rhythm figure 4a   *end Rhythm figure 4a*

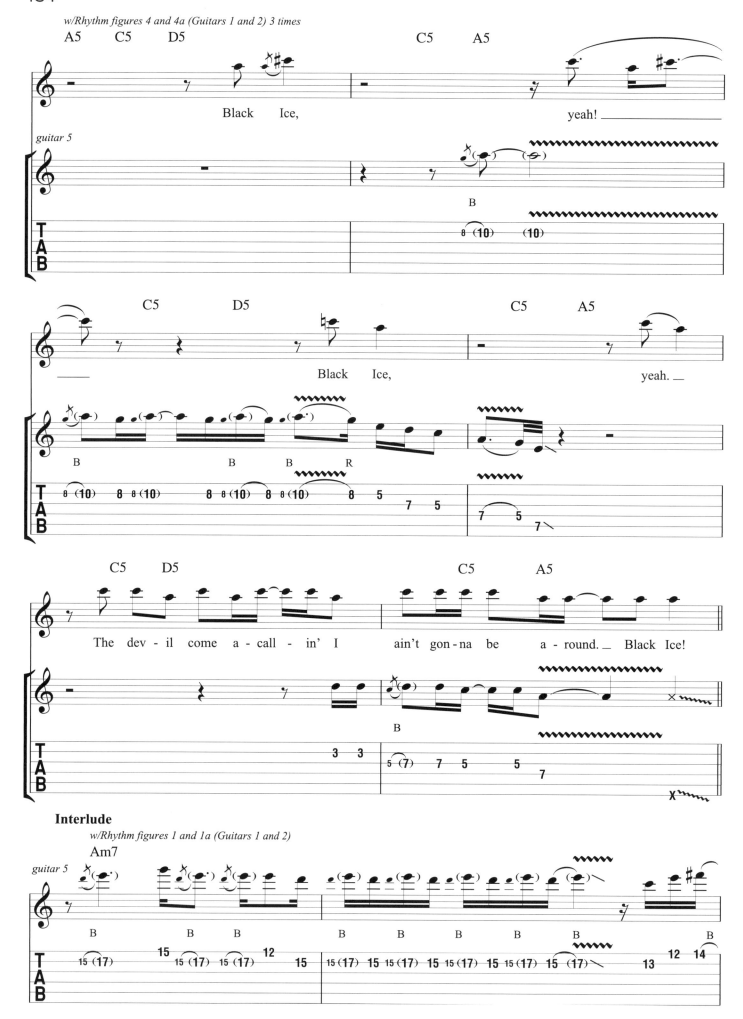

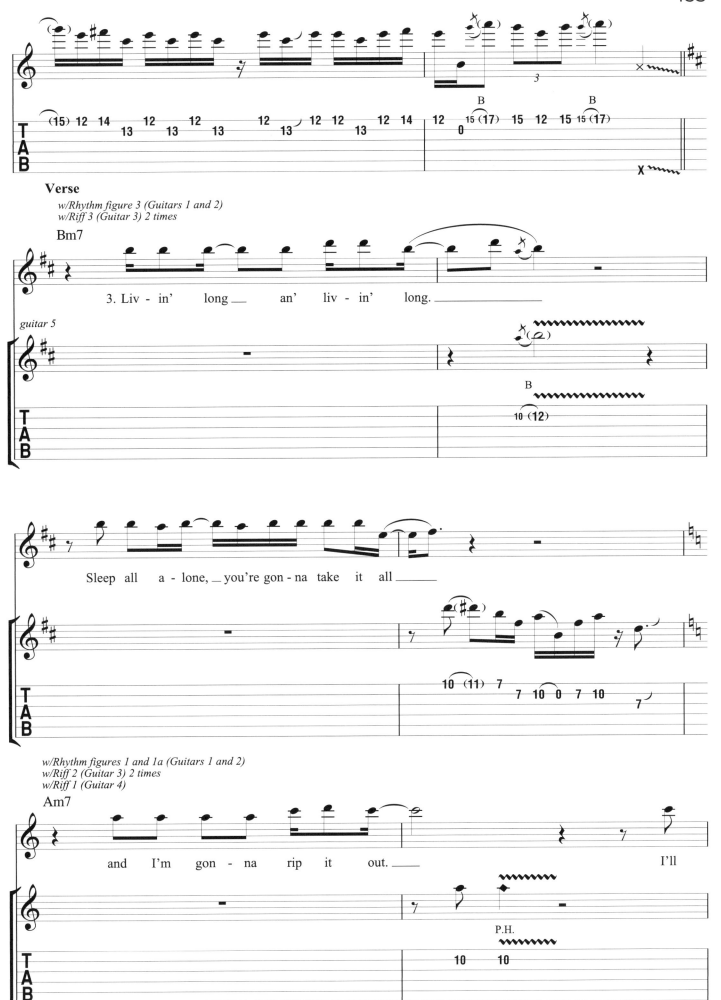

kick, I'll creep-crawl down your street, I'll gouge your eyes ___ out, ___ yeah! ___

Chorus

w/Rhythm figures 4 and 4a (Guitars 1 and 2) 4 times

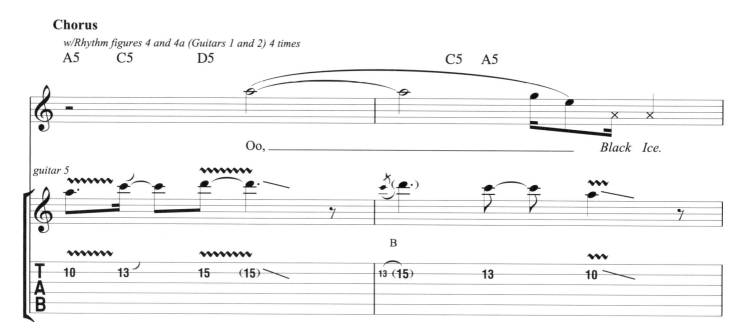

Oo, _____ *Black Ice.*

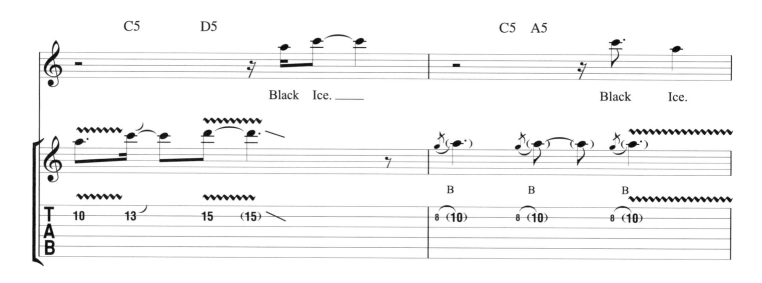

Black Ice. ___   Black Ice.

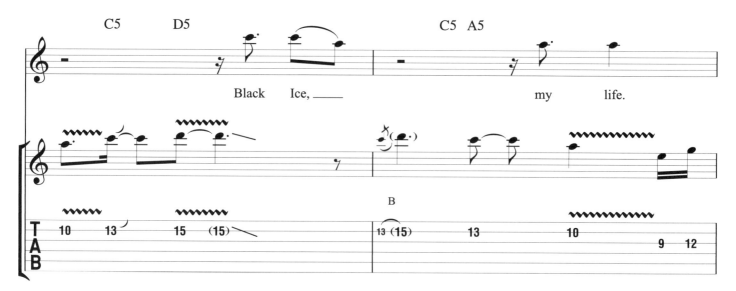

Black Ice, ___   my life.

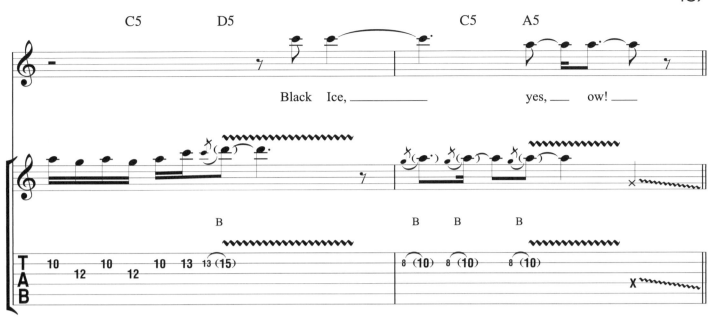

Interlude

w/Rhythm figure 1a (Guitars 1 and 2)

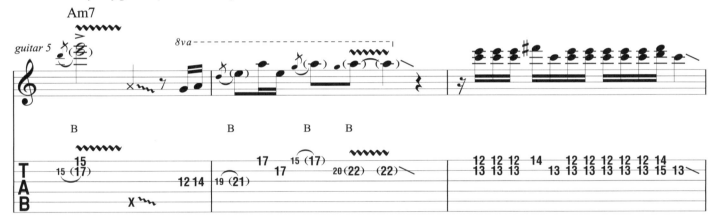

Outro Chorus

w/Rhythm figure 1a (Guitar 1)
w/Riff 2 (Guitar 3) 3 1/2 times
w/Riff 1 (Guitar 4) 1 3/4 times

Ice, my life.

guitar 5

hold bend

guitar 2

w/Rhythm figure 1 (Guitar 1) 1st 3 meas.

A5 C5 A5

Oo.

hold bend

When the dev - il come a - call - in' I

A5 C5 A5

A5 C5 A5

ain't gon - na be a - round. I'll kick, I'll creep - crawl down your street an'

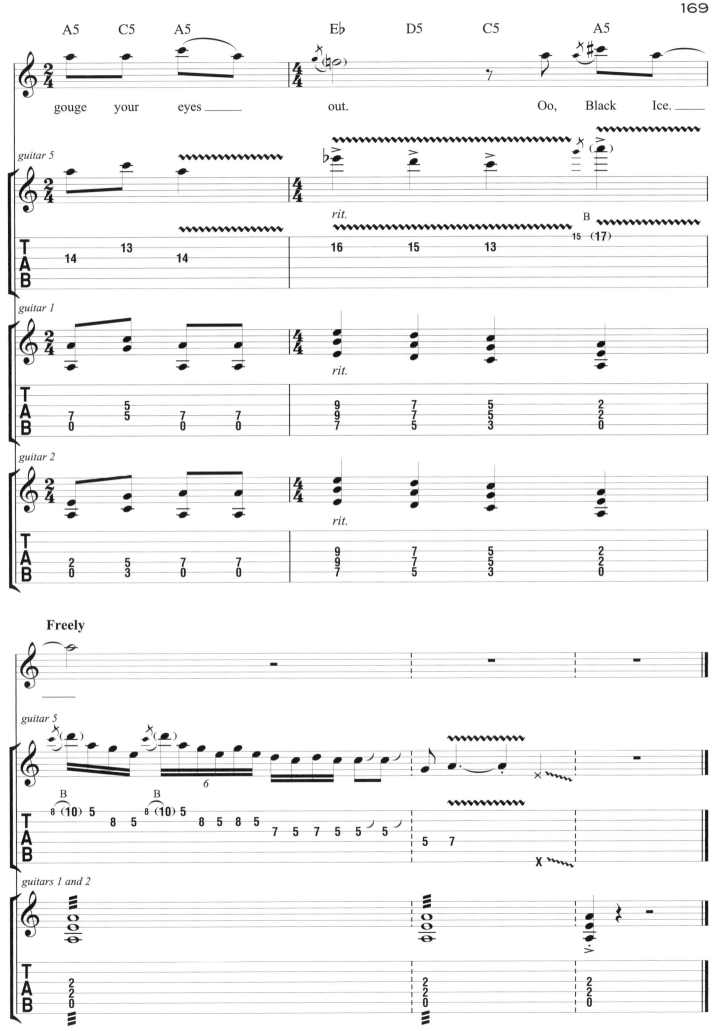

LEGEND OF MUSIC SYMBOLS

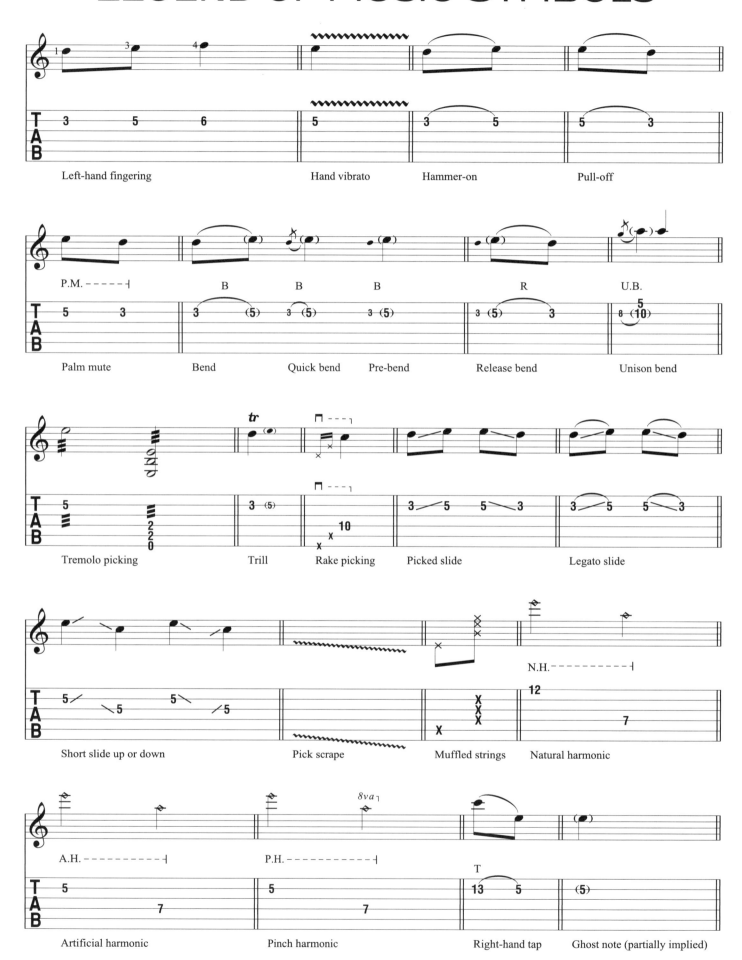